Eden Was No Garden

NIGEL CALDER Eden

An Inquiry

Was No Garden

into the Environment of Man

HOLT, RINEHART AND WINSTON

New York   Chicago   San Francisco

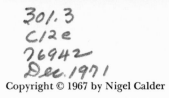

Copyright © 1967 by Nigel Calder

Library of Congress Catalog Card Number: 67-14655

First Edition

8644650

Printed in the United States of America

Preface

IF MEN were intended to work the soil they would have longer arms. In truth, we evolved as hunters and we remain the most efficient predatory animals of all, shrewd of brain, infinitely adaptable of body, and with hands to make and wield weapons. Yet since the invention of agriculture some 10,000 years ago, most men have been obliged to bend their straight backs to cultivate the land. We have grown mightily in numbers, and have constructed remarkable civilizations on the basis of agriculture. But we have made it a distinctly boring world for most people; only in sport and in war can we recapture something of the excitement of the chase, which was the everyday occupation of the first of our species.

It is a good moment to reconsider how we should live. In the first place, we have recently acquired some astonishing powers. We can get energy from its ultimate source, the annihilation of matter in nuclear reactions. We can modify the heredity of plants and animals. In the computer we have a machine more revolutionary even than the steam engine. In short, we have a torrent of knowledge and skills at our disposal, to shape our civilization along quite novel lines. Yet there is little sense of direction or purpose; instead of guiding the torrent we are being swept along by it to some unknown destination. Unless we start picking and choosing between the technological courses open to us, we shall shortly finish up with an ugly, noisy, overcrowded, hungry, chaotic world. The present trends point to affluence and boredom for the richer countries, a tightening grip of poverty and righteous envy on the part of the less fortunate, with intensifying nationalistic policies reinforced by technological competition and a spread of nuclear weapons. Yet we have the means at our disposal to make it quite otherwise.

A second compelling reason for looking with a fresh mind at the roots of our civilization is that agriculture is simply failing us. Only by the very greatest efforts can it provide adequate food for the growing population in the under-developed countries, and after twenty years of talking about the "problem" there is still no sign that such efforts will be made. The obstacles are human rather than technical; so it is appropriate to look for alternative methods of producing food that may encounter fewer social obstacles. Such methods exist, or can be invented.

Thirdly, there is the ever present risk of annihilation. Men, the hunters-*manqués*, have put such intellectual and physical resources into hunting their fellow-men that we can now conceivably achieve what all our natural enemies have failed in—our own total extinction. Short of that (which is technically a little awkward) we can wreak unimaginable suffering on our own kind, and devastate our own works. We know it perfectly well, yet we do not shrink from the preparations, because warfare continues to fascinate us. In nations, as in individuals, readiness to fight is still regarded as a mainstay of honour. Only if we give due weight and outlet to the manly aggressive instincts of the hunter in each of us can we hope to avoid a disaster. A policy so based is entirely feasible.

These three apparently diverse considerations converge on a single technical question: whether the widespread cultivation of the soil remains the most appropriate source of our first physical requirement—our food. And it is around the negative answer to this question that this book revolves.

In arguing for the replacement of most of agriculture by artificial methods of food production, I am conscious that it will seem so profound a change to many people that it could easily acquire the status of a dogma, a heresy, or a panacea. I hope that it will not be taken in any of those glib senses. It is neither an original proposal (see Bibliographical Note below), nor is it essential in the sense that no other course is conceivable. The choice is not between 100 per cent agriculture or 100 per cent synthetic food; rather it is a matter of deciding, in something which is more than a prediction but less than a policy, what the balance between the two sources should be. Certainly I should regret it bitterly if the proposition about synthetic food should be seized upon by people incapable of distinguishing between the short-term and the long-term, as a distraction from the immediate task of developing agricultural food production as rapidly as possible.

Because I believe strongly that too many discussions of future possibilities are narrowly and therefore falsely based on one or two "bright ideas", this book broadens out from a discussion of agriculture and its replacement for a conspectus of other, simultaneous trends that have to be harmonized in that world of our children and grandchildren.

Despite these disclaimers, I am out to persuade. Synthetic food production deserves a massive programme of research, development, and application, here and now. And although others have casually or earnestly discussed the possibilities, as far as I know this book is the first attempt to consider them against the broad panorama of our skills and needs. In making the attempt it has become apparent to me that the liberation of large areas of the planet's surface could enable us, in the nick of time, to reconstruct our way of life.

BIBLIOGRAPHICAL NOTE

There have been many allusions to the general possibilities of synthetic food production, as well as an extensive specialized literature on individual techniques. Here is a selection of typical references from the former group:

BERNAL, J. D. (1958). *World Without War* (London, Routledge & Kegan Paul), pp. 271–6.

A brisk canter (characteristic of the author) through the subject, in the course of which he remarks: "Field agriculture is in direct contradiction to the whole tendency of modern industry, which is to limit the volume of the working space and to maximalize the output by carrying out reactions quickly instead of having to wait for the cycle of the year."

BROWN, H., BONNER, J., and WEIR, J. (1957). *The Next Hundred Years* (London, Weidenfeld & Nicolson), pp. 76–78.

A sceptical view: "The chemical synthesis of food would also appear to be an exceedingly remote possibility, at least so far as provision of general diet calories is concerned."

FOOD AND AGRICULTURE ORGANIZATION, Rome (1965). *The State of Food and Agriculture*, p. 107.

A summary of some current lines of research, concluding: "In general, technology is not a limiting factor in developing food products from unconventional sources. The most critical and difficult aspect in introducing these products for large-scale use in the human diet is acceptability and marketing."

Fox, B. A. and Cameron, A. G. (1961). *A Chemical Approach to Food and Nutrition* (London University Press), pp. 300–3.

An example of how the idea of synthetic food is creeping into undergraduate textbooks.

Huxley, Aldous (1932). *Brave New World* (London), chapter 16.

The case against synthetic food, in the year of Our Ford 632: ". . . 'The Inventions Office is stuffed with plans for labour-saving processes. Thousands of them.' Mustapha Mond made a lavish gesture. 'And why don't we put them into execution? For the sake of the labourers; it would be sheer cruelty to afflict them with excessive leisure. It's the same with agriculture. We could synthesize every morsel of food if we wanted to. But we don't. We prefer to keep a third of the population on the land. For their own sakes—because it takes *longer* to get food out of the land than out of the factory. . .'."

McPherson, A. T. (1965). *Bulletin of the Atomic Scientists* (Chicago), vol. 21, no. 7, pp. 6–11, "Synthetic food for tomorrow's billions".

A very penetrating, if brief review of the whole subject, in which the author concludes: "Thus, the synthesis of food is not merely a possible development at some distant time. A crisis is approaching. A new, little-known, untried but feasible solution is available. The question is whether the leaders of nations will recognize and avail themselves of this solution in time."

Thomson, Sir George (1955). *The Foreseeable Future* (Cambridge), pp. 113–16.

Here is an author who emphasizes the recreational aspect: "It ought to be possible to allow much of England to return to parkland and to let the downs go back to grass. Large herds of cattle, fed mostly on synthetic foods delivered automatically at distributing centres, and unused to man, will roam through the trees as they did long ago. Is it too much to hope that hunting with the bow and arrow will revive as a means of procuring food from these herds and supplying the chemical engineers who made the fodder with a spice of adventure?"

Waddington, C. H. (1965). *The World in 1984* (Narmondsworth, Pelican Books, ed. N. Calder), vol. 2, p. 13, "Science and Wisdom".

"Of course it is conceivable that by 1984 we shall produce our food in factories, without animals or plants, exploiting the most far-reaching biological discovery of the last few years, the synthesis of proteins in cell-free systems. . . . But that technological dream is nearer fifty than twenty years ahead, unless resources are put into these lines of research at something like the level that was used to develop the atom bomb."

Contents

It may be that to relate population to environment optimally is the greatest technological task to the end of this century.

LORD FLOREY, *co-discoverer of penicillin, in his final address as President of the Royal Society, 1965*

CHAPTER 1

The Failure to Feed

THE SPACEMAN viewing the Earth, the Blue Planet, from his capsule confirms by direct perception what the sages of many centuries have known by deduction: that we inhabit a film of life on the surface of a relatively small stony sphere. In a sense, to travel round the world in ninety minutes is to diminish it; on the minds of Magellan's seamen, arriving in Seville in 1522 after the first circumnavigation, the great size of the globe had impressed itself in a tragic three-year voyage. Whether the Earth seems big or small depends on one's mode of transport. For the businessman in a jet plane or the war-lord with his intercontinental missiles it is compact enough; for the villager on the Asian plateau or in the heart of Africa, moving on foot or by animal cart, it appears unbounded.

The sense of agoraphobia or claustrophobia also depends on a reading of statistics. Being told that the number of human beings on Earth will double in thirty to forty years may evoke casual jokes from rush-hour commuters in a big city. When it is translated into the statement that instead of forty acres of the Earth's total surface area per head, we shall have to make do with twenty acres, the optimist can point to the amount of sunlight falling on the lesser area, compute its theoretical productivity of edible material, by land and sea—and promise plenty for all. The picture becomes grimmer again when one observes that, of those twenty acres, only half an acre is at present under cultivation and the prospects for greatly increasing the area under cultivation are not very bright, at least in this century. In the race between population and food production, it now looks very probable that the food producers will lose.

The face of hunger is ugly. Children suffering from gross malnutrition—clinical cases of *kwashiorkor*—wear a characteristic look of listless misery. Their hair is mangy, their skin a patchy red. The condition is common among infants of poor countries who are displaced from their mothers' breasts by a new-born brother or sister. Such children are critically ill, and although when they die some infectious disease or other may be blamed, the real reason is lack of proper food. The medicine is simple: cow's milk. For want of cow's milk or its equivalent, many children die; many more grow up physically and mentally weakened.

The landscapes of hunger are not pretty, although they sometimes appear picturesque to the traveller. From the air, the relative harmony of industry and agriculture is plainly apparent in north-west Europe: the chimneys of steelworks, chemical factories, and power stations rise cosily among kempt fields and orchards. Here is the natural cradle of a way of life which Europeans have wished on the rest of the world. Over Italy and Greece, the former Arcadia, the picture changes and under the warm sun the land looks weary, with dust covering it like verdigris. The ancient lands—the plains of Tigris and Indus, Ganges and Nile—where man has farmed for millennia, still give for all their antiquity an impression of perennial struggle to keep back the desert; outside the

cities the dwellings are ephemeral and the farms makeshift. Beside the Indus, in West Pakistan, one can see
soil whitened with salt and other fields waterlogged, as a
result of over-irrigation. Almost everywhere in the Old
World, beyond the rich, modern farms of Europe, agriculture is a grim business; and often the soil has been
devastated by bad farming and consequent erosion. Large
tracts of Latin America, too, are farmed by impoverished
tenants. Only in the wheatlands of North America,
perhaps, does agriculture acquire magnificence.

Ugly, too, is the political face of hunger. In 1964,
Indonesia attempted ludicrously small and ill-organized
raids across the Malacca Strait to Malaya. When, at the
beginning of 1965, Malaysia was given a seat on the
Security Council, Indonesia, a country desperately
dependent on international aid and good-will, left the
United Nations. In the early 1960s Indonesia's population
had grown faster than her food production—and this in a
nation already at the bottom of the tables of protein intake
per head. The price of rice trebled within a year; inflation
left the country's eight-year development plan in ruins.
The last thing Indonesia needed was new territory; apart
from the overpopulated Java and Bali, her territories in
Sumatra, Borneo, and Celebes, and in the 2,000 other
islands of the volcanic chain, were largely undeveloped.
Yet, in her nibbles at Malaysia and her boasts about being
able to make nuclear weapons, she gave the world a fore-
taste of quarrels that will surely come, between poor
nations as well as between poor and rich, as the race
against hunger is lost.

The principal failure of agriculture can be summed up
in two words that should be as fearful for us as "hydrogen
bomb" or "bubonic plague": protein deficiency.

Proteins, which are of many different kinds, are the chief structural and metabolic agents of the human body. Manufactured within the living cells of the body, under the intimate authority of the nucleic acids that embody our genetic inheritance, proteins make us. Their two chief manifestations are as the enzymes which govern the myriad of chemical reactions involved in the business of living, and as structures—whether in the intricate architecture of the individual cell or in the large-scale strength of muscle, skin, or hair.

Our own proteins are manufactured in little "workshops" within each living cell, called ribosomes. The raw materials from which the proteins are made are amino acids obtained primarily by the digestion of the proteins in the food that we eat. There are about twenty different kinds of amino acids involved and they are arranged in subtle sequence into chains having precisely the right physical and chemical properties for the functions they have to perform. The elucidation of the machinery whereby this task is done is among the most striking developments of current science.

But without adequate protein foods in the diet, to provide the parts for human proteins, these wonderful mechanisms become like the industries of a beleaguered city. Production slows down in the face of critical shortages of particular parts; with a flurry of improvisation the necessary has to make way for the essential in the tables of priority. In human terms, this means that growth and action are sacrificed to survival. The outward signs are of a wasting body, lethargic movement, and dulled eyes; unseen, the metabolism is working harder than ever to maintain life.

With its powers of recuperation, the body can conceal

the effects of protein deprivation during critical periods of infancy and adolescence. The adult looks whole—a little small, perhaps, and rather lazy and stupid, but the most charitable Westerner may merely assume that these are characteristics of the hungry man's race. Is it not remarkable, in a post-Freudian world, when Western parents are acutely conscious of how relatively trivial deprivations of childhood can permanently affect the mind, that we hear so little about the psychological and neurological effects of chronic malnutrition in the children of poorer countries?

Protein is ubiquitous. Every plant and animal contains it and so, therefore, does every dish that people eat. But there is protein and protein. The twenty or so key amino acids shared by virtually all living things occur in different proportions in the proteins of different species. The most important differences in proportion are between plants and animals. Animals have, by and large, similar protein compositions. Hen's egg and cow's milk have almost precisely the same proportions of the various amino acids as the human body. Meat and fish are little different. People can live perfectly well on an unvaried diet based on any one of these animal protein foods. But plants are much less standardized in their proteins, so that a given plant does not contain anything like the same proportions of the amino acids. Usually some will be there in relative excess, while others will be depleted. Moreover, plant proteins are less readily digested.

As a result, there is no cultivated plant anything like as nutritious in respect of protein as foods derived from animals. To give an example, a relative deficiency in particular amino acids means that one has to eat 30 per cent more rice protein than egg protein to secure the same protein intake—and, because the protein in rice is less concentrated, the weight of food that has to be eaten is more than twice as great. Of course, the carbohydrate in the rice is useful, too, but a person, particularly a child, cannot eat an unlimited quantity of food. Rice is among the better sources of plant protein.

No matter how abundant some of the amino acids may be, they can be used in protein synthesis only in proportion to the least abundant. There is a time factor: the amino acids which cannot be used in protein synthesis are broken down or eliminated by the body. Roughly speaking, the protein value of lunch depends on the amino acids present in the lunch, not on breakfast or supper. (The same is not true for vitamins or for energy-giving foods, which are husbanded by the body.)

If one plant food lacks particular amino acids, it is legitimate to look for other plants which have those amino acids present in excess, with a view to blending them in a composite food resembling animal protein. For example, soya is short of sulphur-containing amino acids but rich in lysine; in sesame it is the other way about. Vegetarians do well enough, provided they can afford a variety of different plant foods—also provided they are not too strict about it, for unless they include a little food derived from animals (milk, say) they may suffer from vitamin B_{12} deficiency, and perhaps from deficiencies of other essential substances not yet identified by the dieticians. The United Nations Children's Fund, and other bodies, have made a substantial effort to pioneer milk substitutes based upon such composites.

There have also been developments aimed at concentrating plant proteins. Particularly notable for its concept is N. W. Pirie's machine at Rothamsted which extracts protein from leaves by rupturing the cells. In principle it could be used to get food from leaves that are at present ignored as being indigestible. More elaborate processes are available for extracting and purifying protein from oil seeds as a by-product of the vegetable oil industry.

The comparison of proteins from different sources is complicated by the fact that the human body can convert some amino acids into others. There seems to be a real minimum of eight amino acids which have to be obtained from food. But I doubt if anyone would recommend a protein diet based only on these.

The extent of the world's "protein gap" is difficult to measure, because we cannot be too sure of the protein requirements of different communities in different climates, nor of the precise nutritional value of different foods, nor of how fairly a nation's consumption of protein is shared among people of different ages, social classes, and occupations. But the national averages are revealing. In the countries of Western Europe and North America average protein intakes are roughly 150–200 per cent of the calculated requirements. Where people can afford to buy the food they think they need, this seems to be the natural "ceiling". In many other countries, the average protein intake is almost exactly the same as the calculated minimum requirements. Only if the food were shared according to a system of strict rationing by age group and body weight would everyone get enough protein. Accordingly we must suppose that very many people do not have enough. Countries in this category include India, Pakistan, Ceylon, Indonesia, Colombia, and Peru.

That is the situation for total protein. When we look at animal protein things are worse. If we consider again what the prosperous countries eat—which is as good a test as any of what reasonable appetite demands—we find that the average intakes are around half a kilogram per person per day. In Africa, the Near East, and the Far East, the averages are commonly one-fifth of that, in some countries much less.

Reasons for the difference in animal-protein standards are not hard to find. Livestock production in the poorer countries is chiefly a matter of putting animals out to graze. In the richer countries, huge tracts of cultivated land are devoted to growing grain to feed to the livestock; indeed, in Western Europe and North America more grain is eaten by animals than by human beings. Where there is barely enough grain for people, how can you feed it to animals? Other reasons include animal diseases, and social customs which encourage people to maintain large numbers of unproductive animals, for reasons of prestige or religion.

To bring the whole world into line with the animal-protein standards of, say, Britain, would require the world's livestock industry to produce two-and-a-half times as much as it is doing. To provide such standards for the doubled population of AD 2000 would be Herculean. Not only is present animal production inadequate, that which is produced costs too much, so that protein consumption is proportional to income rather than to need, up to a level of satiation.

The tersest summary of the requirements in the next twenty years is given by Dr B. R. Sen, Director-General of the Food and Agriculture Organization, writing in 1964:

Taking into account both population changes and the need to improve existing diets, the total food supplies of the less developed regions of the world need to be *two and a quarter times* their existing level by 1984. This increase is in total food supply. The supply of foods of animal origin in the less developed regions of the world would need to be increased to *three times* their existing level. For the world as a whole by 1984, total food supplies would need to be *one and three-quarter times* the existing level and animal foods *nearly doubled* (*New Scientist*, vol. 21, p. 270).

These are not merely targets, but demands. The population of the under-developed countries is going to grow by about 70 per cent in the twenty-year period. The disproportionate increases are to allow for bringing diets up to the basic nutritional needs. It would be politically intolerable if three-quarters of the world's population, in twenty years' time, were to be living in countries unable to meet the minimum diets for good health.

Dr Sen estimates that, even given "dramatic efforts", the demands can only be met on a world-wide scale if about 10 per cent of the world's food is in the form of exports from the developed to the "developing" countries. In Latin America and Africa he thinks that regional production and needs can be made to match; in the Near East and Far East he does not. Taking the under-developed regions together, he expects an increase in food production of 85 per cent. That would do little more than keep abreast of population.

We should be clear that Dr Sen's estimates, while cautious, are essentially optimistic, assuming as he does that the necessary efforts can and will be made and affirming that there is little doubt that technically the overall increases can be achieved. But what is technically possible and what will happen are very different matters.

For the past twenty years, distinguished men all over the world have sounded the alarm about world food supplies. For twenty years, international efforts have been made to get a rapid expansion in food production. The 1960s have been designated the UN Development Decade. To meet Dr Sen's figures, food production in the under-developed regions has to increase by 50 per cent (compound) per decade; foods of animal origin by more than 70 per cent. The corresponding figures for the past decade (despite all the fuss) have been roughly half these. They have just about kept abreast of rising populations, but have not allowed any improvement in average diets.

Dr Sen sees hope in "the changing attitudes and aspirations of the people". I do not. I have looked in vain for any real sign, even in the comparatively generous efforts of the United States, of adequate measures to get agricultural production soaring in the under-developed countries. It seems to me that conditions were in some ways more propitious ten years ago than now. In those days, before the Congo disaster, before the Sino-Indian and Indo-Pakistani wars, before the crises of Cuba, Indonesia, and Viet-Nam, it was possible to believe that the money disbursed in aid through the UN and bilateral agreements would work its magic, that the former colonial powers, the other advanced countries, and the under-developed countries themselves would realize their common interest in food production. Today we see neo-nationalism and neo-colonialism at work, new wars and threats of war, and a fatal indifference in high places to the simple need to grow food.

It is not enough to fret about food production. Agriculture has other purposes; indeed, in the thinking of administrators in under-developed countries, exportable raw materials like rubber, cotton, jute, wool and hides, fats and oils, may take precedence over food production. For such agricultural products mean foreign exchange. The underfed plantation worker living in the midst of productive land devoted to cash crops for export is an all too common phenomenon. So we must not lose sight of this other side of agriculture, which accounts for about a quarter of the world's agricultural trade. But we can say at once that the long-term prospects for these natural products as a source of wealth are extremely black, because in every case man-made materials with approximate or notably better properties are becoming available.

In a rational world, no man would starve to allow productive land to be used for obtaining materials which can be made economically in chemical factories. Indeed, chemical research workers, far from accepting the chiding that they are stealing the traditional sources of income of the poorer countries, claim that they are increasing the land available for food production. In principle they are right, but in practice the producers of agricultural raw materials are desperately anxious to ward off the effects of scientific competition, especially in countries like Malaysia whose economies are founded upon "cash crops". Canute could have taught them better. The natural rubber producers point triumphantly to the fact that they have maintained their level of production over the last fifteen years, in the face of competition from synthetic rubber. But they have done so only because of big increases in demand from the Communist bloc. In that period rubber consumption has roughly doubled, and the whole of the increase is accounted for by synthetics. Although there will be a strong demand for natural rubber for some years, it is only a matter of time before the decline sets in. Already three-quarters of the rubber used in the United States is synthetic.

Rubber, in fact, is the really dramatic case because, while other man-made materials have somewhat different properties from the natural materials they challenge, synthetic rubber can now be made which is chemically identical with natural rubber. This is made possible by one of the most remarkable discoveries in chemistry since the war—the techniques, which won a Nobel prize for Giulio Natta, whereby chemical units making up long, chain-like molecules of plastics or rubber can be arranged with complete regularity. But while "stereo-regular poly-isoprene" duplicates natural rubber, there are other synthetic rubbers which have important advantages over natural rubber for specific purposes. Thus, styrene-butadiene rubber is less resilient than natural rubber, but wears better; butyl rubber is less permeable to air, while neoprene has proved particularly good for soles of shoes.

At the other extreme, among the natural products, leather has perhaps been technically the most resistant to imitation, because of the texture which makes it water-proof and yet able to "breathe". Accordingly, leather still holds its own in the uppers of shoes, and in gloves. In many other uses, including the soles of shoes and suitcases, synthetic rubbers and plastics have largely replaced leather. And the chemists have not been idle; already there are synthetic materials matching the special qualities of leather required for uppers and, when these have become commercially acceptable, the trade in hides and skins must eventually begin to decline.

Synthetic fibres are only now beginning to acquire the agreeable "feel" of, say, wool, and in many uses they are still mixed with natural fibres. Their toughness, crease resistance, and smart appearance (in nylon stockings, for example) have been more than enough, however, to out-weigh the disadvantages of the earlier synthetic fibres, so much so that world production of them is doubling and redoubling every three and a half years. So far, the demand for clothes has been so great in the post-war world that there has not been an actual decline in the demand for cotton, wool, or rayon—which last, for our purposes, should be counted as a natural fibre, as it is made from cellulose. But the rates of growth have been incomparably less.

Where we do see an actual cut-back of demand for natural products is in the fats and oils used for making soap. Synthetic detergents are simply better as cleaning agents than soap; in principle this is true even of toilet soap, which is harmful to some skins, but manufacturers have not yet been very successful in making detergent-cakes to the liking of the public. Fats and oils are also threatened on another front by the new "plastic" paints.

Finally, what about wood? It is a versatile and useful material, the demand for which grows steadily (in the case of wood for paper-making, alarmingly fast). Much of it comes from regions that are better suited to growing trees than to other purposes. Yet even with wood, one may wonder how long it will be before it is displaced from purposes such as building and furniture-making by plastics and other materials. The future of paper is very uncertain: on the one hand, paper is finding new uses (in clothing, for example) which could increase the demand hugely; on the other hand, it is now conceivable that, with the development of computers and related systems, paper will soon cease to be the chief means of recording and transmitting information and even newspapers may disappear. Moreover, although there is no obvious synthetic substitute for wood pulp in paper-making, it can hardly be expected to escape the continuing attention of materials chemists.

The true situation of these natural products is obscured by the rise in population and in living standards that keeps the demand for them growing, while the artificial replacements, invented in many cases only in the past ten years or so, have not yet been accepted everywhere. As the new chemical products become both better and cheaper than the old natural ones, the era of cotton and rubber, of wool and soap, must soon draw to a close, unless it is artificially prolonged by people desperate to preserve raditional ways of life.

No adequate synthetic substitute yet exists for the food produced by agriculture. In time that too will come. Meanwhile agriculture is failing; the farmers in most parts of the world are simply unable to feed the growing billions. Chief among the reasons for this failure of agriculture has been near indifference on the part of the governments of many of the under-developed countries. In too many cases, they are much more concerned with politics and with the grander manifestations of development—steelworks and power stations—than with food. In countries which have been malnourished for many years there is something near to acceptance of poor diets. Sometimes social traditions or caste put agriculture beneath the notice of the high-born. Rulers are anxious to surround themselves with the superficial symbols of the developed nations: jet airliners and jet fighters, nuclear reactors and smart hotels. If one complains about all this, one is accused of wanting to keep the under-developed countries "in their place", to prevent them rivalling the advanced countries in their industry and prestige. The fact is that priorities have gone awry.

The government of India, under its Third Five-Year Plan, spent more on nuclear research than it did on agricultural research. Only one-fifth of public investment under the plan was devoted to agriculture, although the majority of the Indian working population was engaged on the land. It is a hopeful sign that, in the Fourth Plan, agriculture has a bigger share of investment. Governments of under-developed countries devoting markedly less than 20 per cent of their development budgets to agriculture include Chile, Indonesia, and Thailand. Others devoting more than 30 per cent to agriculture are few, but include Cyprus, Jordan, Syria, Madagascar, and Upper Volta. Yet Dr Stefan Dedijer (*New Scientist*, vol. 21, p. 461) has pointed out that no fewer than fifty-seven countries (including Afghanistan and Honduras) have atomic energy commissions.

In the developed countries agriculture has in no sense failed, but it has changed astonishingly. Science, industry, and marketing have formed a powerful alliance of skills around the farmer. The chemical industry provides the farmer with a range of potent agents: fertilizers and soil conditioners; weed-killers and pesticides; antibiotics and vaccines. Machines plough the fields, reap the harvest, milk the cows, dig the ditches. Modern scientific farming is dedicated to the production of crops of standard quality under controlled conditions. Virtually everything except the weather is a matter of calculation.

The land has come to be treated as a huge, two-dimensional biochemical factory powered by sunlight. In it, weeds and wildlife have no place amid the broad acres of carefully evolved crops. Animal husbandry has become a matter of weighing machines, with diets calculated by computer and with artificial environments created to encourage production. There is nothing inherently wrong with these developments; on the contrary they have provided the most efficient means of producing food. But it is as well that we should recognize them, so that when we come to consider the future of agriculture we should not be misled into any sentimentality about the jumbled crops and raucous farmyards of children's picture-books (see also Chapter 6).

However, the production of food in the developed countries could be greatly increased. For example, Britain at present imports about half her food, but in an emergency she could get by (given rationing) with almost no imports—a possibility that was seriously contemplated in the darkest days of the Second World War. The United States and Australia already produce great surpluses on the basis of extensive, labour-sparing agriculture. Intensive farming (where the soils can take it) might easily double or treble production. The Soviet Union is, agriculturally, in a somewhat under-developed state; but, whatever the short-term set-backs in the virgin-lands policy have been, that and the "chemicalization" of Soviet agriculture now in progress should lead to great increases in the harvests.

In theory, the developed countries could easily make up the food deficits of the under-developed regions. In practice, after twenty years of attempts to find an economic basis for that solution, it is reasonable to doubt whether it will be done. Fragments of policy appear, for example, in the United States government's scheme for giving away surplus food in lieu of financial aid. Under-developed countries do import food for famine relief and do so increasingly on a routine basis, but the economic burden is very heavy. As I have mentioned, Dr Sen thinks that in twenty years' time we should expect 10 per cent of the world's food production to take the form of exports from the developed to the under-developed regions; but, unless there is remarkable economic progress in the latter, it is hard to see how it can be paid for. We should not regard this aspect of the situation as a failure of agriculture itself, nor as a want of humanity on the part of the surplus producers; the bankers and economists have simply failed to invent the financial tricks for transferring surpluses to empty stomachs. I would rate it the biggest single failure of the human intellect in the post-war period. In the absence of any such solution, the basic motive of agricultural research and improvement within the developed countries is less to enlarge food production than to make it more profitable.

CHAPTER 2

Eden was no Garden

IN EVERYTHING that has been written and said about the
race between the USSR and the USA to put a man on the
moon, it seems to me that the most interesting question
of all has been overlooked.

However much the space enthusiasts may try to talk
around it, and suggest more practical motives, everyone
else knows that the chief reason why the governments of
these two nations have invested so much of their nations'
wealth in this hasty competition is the desire for prestige.
The Americans could properly have claimed that their
initial scientific satellites and planetary probes, and their
communications and weather satellites, were more useful
to mankind than the Soviet programme with its emphasis
on manned space flight. Yet President Kennedy, in making his reluctant decision to send men to the moon at
fantastic expense, recognized that many people in the
under-developed, uncommitted world, who had most to
lose from a diversion of resources into a space race, were
more impressed by the Soviet space exploits than by all
the billions of dollars poured out in foreign aid by the
American taxpayers.

The neglected question is this: why are people so
impressed? Why, in other words, is there prestige to be
won in space? For, however much humanitarians or

cynics may scoff, the fact is that the cheers ring around the world for the spacemen.

For scientific man, the race to the moon is an extremely dubious operation. For agricultural man the cheering makes no sense when money is needed to water and fertilize the fields. We can understand the prestige of the spaceman only if we accept that it is the hunter in mankind who is cheering. He cheers as he must have cheered the discoverer of a new hunting ground, or the daring soul who first rode on the water on a log, or the man who shot the first arrow high into the air. Indeed, in the very irrationality of the exploration of space at a time of terrestrial crisis, we see the repudiation of agrarian standards.

In this chapter, I shall discuss human nature and attitudes, and how they were modified by the needs of agriculture.

Living in trees is good for you. To move about on a tree without falling off requires firmness of grip and dexterity of limb and eye. Accordingly it is not surprising that the most artful animal of all evolved from tree-dwelling apes. Nature's great invention involved, among other developments, the transition from a hand that could grasp a bough to one that could wield either a club ("power grip") or a small flint ("precision grip").

The details of how and where the successive species leading to modern man came into being can cheerfully be left to palaeontologists wrangling over scraps of bone. Even the last step, to *Homo sapiens* himself, is wrapped in obscurity; and, until there is vastly more evidence, human evolution is in the same category of speculation as the nature of the universe or the interior of the Earth. But evolve man did, and we cannot begin to understand ourselves, our behaviour, or our aspirations until we have considered the way of life to which this superior ape was adapted at the outset. Evolution is usually a slow business and, however sophisticated and artificial our society may be, our bodies are largely indistinguishable from those of our Palaeolithic ancestors; by implication, our brains are little different. But those early men did not work the soil.

Agriculture is an invention of man, not man of agriculture. If the possibilities of cultivating and using crop plants were self-evident in the environment of the early primates, an agricultural ape might have evolved in our place. But it would be a very different animal. It would not stand erect, and it would have longer arms than we have. Its fingers would be better suited to digging. In place of the highest mental faculties, it would be better off with strong instinctual patterns of crop-tending behaviour, an acceptance of what is to us boredom. Human powers of speech, so well adapted to the elaborate manœuvres of a hunting party, would be largely redundant. This hypothetical *Homo agricola* would be better adapted to a vegetarian diet with drastic seasonal variations, and its attitude to other animals would be defensive rather than aggressive. In *Homo sapiens*, the combination of agrarian motives and aggressive habits has been singularly disastrous, less to man himself in his wars than to other species.

As a predatory animal, man the hunter was constrained by the same rules as govern all other beasts of prey. There was a natural limit of population set by the availability of prey; if the hunter killed too many animals too quickly he would starve until the animals were replaced. The human population densities that could be supported by this way of life were very small—typically, perhaps, one person per four square miles, or little more than the density of the lion population in the parks of Africa today.

The details of human evolution can be left to the fossil-hunters, as I have said, but if we are to seek man's true nature, we need to know from them the connection between biological and cultural evolution in the early phases. What did the first representatives of *Homo sapiens* eat? At what stage did fire come under control? The precursors of *Homo sapiens* made tools; did this mean that biological evolution became inseparable from the tools, so that man should be regarded not simply as *the* tool-maker but as a higher, more successful form evolved from the early tool-makers? In short, which came first, modern man or his skills?

The answers to these questions are of particular importance if we are to be sure of the biological basis for man's mentality and feeding habits. According to some, early man was by necessity a vegetarian; his teeth could not cope with raw meat unless there was time to chew for hours on end, and even to skin an animal with inadequate tools would be, on this view, a very difficult task. The trouble with this picture is that you do not need to be brainy to gather fruit and nuts, and something happened during the last phase of human evolution to force an astonishingly rapid development in brain size.

A more credible account would start from the premise that tools were the claws of man's precursors, and they were out for meat. Skill in the making of tools and—how important!—in teaching and planning their manufacture would give its owners a marked advantage compared with clumsier and dimmer-witted relatives. This same ingenuity would enable men to outwit other animals and also to master fire.

Evidence from Choukoutien in China shows that Peking Man (*Pithecanthropus pekinensis*) was making tools from hard stones before *Homo sapiens* appeared on the scene, and had fire, too. Judging from the animal remains associated with him, he lived mainly on venison, but he had also overcome elephants, tigers, and other formidable opponents. He seems, moreover, to have been a cannibal. In other places and at later times, Neanderthal Man was exhibiting similar prowess. The tools and fire that frail-bodied *Homo sapiens* needed if he was to challenge the world preceded him, and he evolved to fit this role, as an artful hunter whose special brain was less important for tool-making than for giving him that social understanding and mastery of casual impulses necessary in a hunting group or society. By the later part of the Palaeolithic period, about 35,000 years ago, there he was, no different from us in body or brain, reigning in Western Asia and Europe, having eclipsed his predecessors.

There is a tendency to think of man the hunter as a poor devil who stalked around for centuries accomplishing nothing of importance until some bright spark invented farming. One reason for this tendency is a confusion between *Homo sapiens* and his predecessors, who stretch back with their rudimentary tools for hundreds of millennia. In fact, when modern man appears he does so with a zest that distinguishes him almost at once. And if we consider how slowly Western civilization developed during the 4,000-odd years from the Early Dynastic times of Sumeria to the Renaissance in Europe, should we not admire the achievements in 25,000 years of small bands of men of the Upper Palaeolithic? They were a relatively new species, and they established themselves with astonishing speed. If we assess human advancement not by simple chronology but in terms of man-years, which enables us to take account of the much smaller populations of the early times, we obtain a better impression of the relative attainments of pre-farming and farming man.

As a hunter, man was very successful. He was equipped with spear-thrower and bow, with flints expertly worked with horn and bone, and with polished stone cut or ground to make novel tools and weapons. The works of art of the Upper Palaeolithic are themselves evidence of a fairly leisured existence and, in Europe at least, life may have been quite agreeable for these hunters. Success is also indicated by geographical spread, from Spain to Siberia, and from the ice front in the north to Afghanistan and Mesopotamia in the south. When the ice retreated the hunters moved north, making a way of life for themselves which to this day has not been successfully challenged, in Arctic conditions, by the farmers. And at some ill-defined time before that, when enough of the world's water was still bottled up in the ice sheets to hold the sea-level low, adventurous men followed the bison and the mammoth across the dried-out Bering Sea into North America, where they turned up on the great plains about 12,000 years ago. They were *Homo sapiens*, and hunters to a man. Farmers would never have made it.

"Look here, upon this picture, and on this; the counterfeit presentment of two brothers." If we pause to salute the hunter, before the Neolithic farmer, with his very different skills and systems, appears on the scene, our purpose is not to suggest an innocent nobility in the hunter, in any Rousseau-like sense. He was a rough, ignorant fellow. Yet when we read the evidence of Palaeolithic archaeology, or accounts of those disappearing remnants of essentially Palaeolithic tribes (the Eskimo, the Australian aborigine, the Bushman of the Kalahari) we find much that is admirable and ingenious.

How do you deal with an angry bull elephant, when all

you have is a sharpened stone? You nip aside, slip in
behind, and cut the tendons of his heel. What can you
do to lure a giraffe, the most timid of large animals? You
play on its curiosity for bright objects by flashing a polished
stone in its direction. The Bushmen, according to Laurens
Van der Post, would use lions as hunting "dogs", letting
them kill game and eat a little, before driving them off
with fire. Franz Boas tells how Eskimo approached deer,
two men together, one stooping behind like the back end
of a pantomime horse, the other carrying his bow on his
shoulders to resemble antlers and grunting like a deer.
The despised Australian aborigine can "travel light" with
only a few wooden and stone implements and, by his
knowledge of nature, survive indefinitely in the Great
Sandy Desert. If we once let these echoes of our prehistory
penetrate our sophisticated heads, they strike in us chords
of excitement, if not of envy.

The orthodox view of the invention of farming sees it as
a prerequisite for the development of civilization. Only
when men were liberated from daily preoccupation with
hunting could they develop an elaborate social life. Moreover, the rise of early cities in Mesopotamia seems to
coincide rather closely with the introduction of agriculture. Yet the idea is now being challenged with the
hypothesis that the first civilized settlements were based
not on cultivation but on highly organized food-gathering.
The point here is that there is no direct evidence of the
actual practice of cultivation in the oldest sites which have
been interpreted as agricultural—only the remains of plants
and animals conventionally associated with farming.

In the Palaeolithic, there were geographical quirks
which gave to some communities huge supplies of wild
animals, as with the Magdelenians in the last Ice Age, and

on such prosperity elaborate cultures and rituals were founded. As some of the Red Indian hunters of North America demonstrated, dense populations were not necessary for the development of a sense of nationhood. There is the more recent evidence that the salmon-eating redskins of British Columbia were so well supplied with food that they developed substantial settlements.

Man's chief physical disadvantage as a hunter must have been the encumbrance of his family. The human infant is uniquely helpless and slow to mature. Accordingly, a fairly settled, well-defended domestic life was necessary from the outset. Women at home minding the children while the men were out hunting were well placed to develop arts like cooking, clothes-making, and pottery, to experiment with new foods, and to discover in their "gardens" the elementary principles of plant reproduction. Jacquetta Hawkes has remarked, "It is tempting to be convinced that the earliest Neolithic societies gave woman the highest status she has ever known" (*Prehistory*, UNESCO History of Mankind).

Agriculture appears to have begun in the Near East about 10,000 years ago, possibly in the Mesopotamian uplands to the east of the Tigris. In this part of southwestern Asia the animals (cattle, sheep, goats, and pigs) and the grasses (ancestors of wheat and barley) were ready to hand in their wild state. There was also an incentive to do something revolutionary about food supplies: as the ice retreated in the northern lands at the end of the last Ice Age, so the climate of the subtropical world turned drier. Game must have become harder to find. Farther north, by contrast, the climate improved for the hunters; the Europeans were slow to adopt agriculture and lagged in many corresponding respects.

However, it was not only in south-western Asia that the inventiveness which led to agriculture was manifest. Hunters of Indo-China discovered rice; their cousins far away in the Americas began to cultivate maize. The invention of agriculture was not an isolated or avoidable event, due to one prehistoric genius; when an intelligent animal appeared capable of accomplishing it, it was inevitable.

Thus agriculture could be described as an evolutionary accident, but an accident having the most profound effects upon man. He bent his back to a self-imposed drudgery. All his culture, his landscapes, and his history came to be shaped by the compulsions of plough and hoe. So conditioned are we still to agriculture that it requires considerable mental effort to escape from its assumptions.

Agriculture was a great success, but at first social organization was inadequate to cope with its consequences. The population of a village could soar in a succession of good years and then face starvation in a bad year. Quite quickly, most of the agricultural land that was accessible was occupied by growing and dividing communities. Conditions were ripe for further developments: the introduction of metals, the building of cities, the organization of large-scale facilities for marketing, storage, and irrigation. Already, within a matter of a millennium or so, the ablest men were being drawn out of farming, into administrative, industrial, or military occupations. The age of the specialist had arrived and farming soon became the task of the lowly.

The development of Sumeria, as the first unquestionable manifestation of civilization, followed quite quickly upon the invention of agriculture; both farming know-how and other forms of culture radiated from there. In the Sumerians, who built their cities and fought their interminable petty wars amid the fields irrigated by Tigris and Euphrates, we recognize our cultural ancestors. They failed in the end—apparently because they over-irrigated and brought underlying salt water to the surface—but not before they had collected a number of important innovations. I say "collected", because some of the crucial elements of Sumerian civilization originated earlier and elsewhere. Coming from the north, apart from farming itself, there were, for example, pottery and weaving; and the Ubaid pioneers themselves brought from the Iranian plateau on the east a knowledge of the metallurgy of copper. The early Sumerians built houses of mud and reeds; they developed irrigation works and took to the rivers in boats; they invented the potter's wheel and soon adapted it to transport. But they also built temples and established an economic and social order run by the priests, which in turn provoked the invention of writing and numerals, for the purpose of keeping accounts. The importance of the calendar in agriculture encouraged rapid and remarkable developments in astronomy.

There were sorrier innovations, too, with the first civilization. Not only was man, the proud hunter, enslaved by the soil, he was enslaved by his fellow-men. The disciplines of irrigation and agriculture, and the need to sustain the surpluses on which the non-farming classes existed, could not rely on instinctive behaviour on the part of the farmers. Feudalism, taxes, and the literal enslavement of prisoners of war were necessary for the system.

Man's success as a hunter must have depended in large measure on co-operation, leadership, loyalty, and planning, and these biologically advantageous qualities were readily adaptable to the artificial requirements of organized farming and city life. How else can we explain the patient acceptance of class divisions, of arbitrary rule, of "justice" flying in the face of reason and humanity that has characterized most of human history, except on the supposition that loyalty to the social unit is generally capable of suppressing other instincts? The hunters had their respected leaders and holy men, but the latter probably never achieved any real tyranny over their fellows. It has taken many millennia of philosophy and revolution to dismantle the outrageous institutions of the kings and priests, created in the immediate wake of agriculture; and if the end is now possibly in sight it is because of the creation of affluence by technologies other than agriculture. Indeed, the ideals if not the practices of welfare capitalism, democratic socialism, and communism can be seen as various attempts to recreate, in the infinitely more complex world of today, something corresponding to the good-natured companionship of the hunting tribe.

We must, of course, distinguish between the consequences of civilization in general, and the particular effects of agriculture as a basis of that civilization. Any analogous system producing plenty of food for growing numbers, through the efforts of part of the population, would have had many comparable effects, good and bad. There are special features of agriculture, however, which have shaped the traditions of men. One of these features is that it is boring.

The earliest phase of farming life in the Neolithic seems to have been perhaps the most placid era of man, if the testimony of the affluent, almost defenceless Danubian sites is to be accepted. But it did not last. With the emergence of civilization there was great opportunity for war, in the form of men and resources to spare—and motive, too, in the form of rivalry between city states and difficulties about the supply of irrigation water and of raw materials for the new industries. The professional soldier made his appearance; he was the hunter in a new and perverted guise, hunter of men. The weapons and the discipline of the hunting-band, wherewith the men of the Upper Palaeolithic had confronted their prey, were refined and turned against other men. The hunters themselves had been no saints, but they simply could not have sustained the chronic warfare that has characterized our civilization from the earliest Sumerian days to the present. The first call on the surplus wealth generated by agriculture has been that of the defence budget.

Yet, although it may seem that organized warfare is a consequence of civilization, rather than of the invention of agriculture, there are good reasons for attaching special significance to the latter. Why are soldiers glamorized? Why are war-narratives and war-movies so gripping? Why do small boys stalk one another with wooden rifles? Surely because the soldier to this day represents that missing hunter in each of us. When the fun (which I take to mean doing what comes naturally) went out of the daily occupations of most men, war provided a direct or vicarious relief of boredom. I do not believe that we shall ever eradicate war, even with the fear of nuclear annihilation, until we have properly diagnosed and treated this ultimate source of war's fascination. Any dreams of world order which seek to bottle up the aggressive urge in man, rather than to canalize it, are likely to fail.

The advent of agriculture also put a new slant on the superstitions of man. The particular rituals of the farming year gave great scope and authority to the priests. But in the mind of the individual farmer there was also a new kind of helplessness, in the face both of the quirks of climate and the tyrannies of man. The male hunter could face disaster on his feet: he, at least, would not quietly starve to death (although his family might) but he could be killed in the course of a desperate attempt to get food. From the evidence of surviving hunting tribes, it appears that the hunter has little fear of death. But the farmer can work skilfully and carefully for a year, and be robbed of his harvest by drought or storm, by locusts or human invaders. Is there not some parallel between diligent work towards a harvest and the preparation for an eventual "judgement" at the end of life?

The God of Moses, at least, is cast in the image of a king who has to be continually appeased; and though the God of Jesus himself is altogether kindlier, the God of Paul has often been presented as a judge of great severity, quick to consign sinners to everlasting damnation. And a feature of the great religions that should give us pause is the notion of God in the image of man. The religion of the hunter typically sees his spirits and totems in the natural world around him. The hunter respects and loves all the works of nature; he treads warily but he kills without malice only what he has to, for survival. For the farmer, it is the works of man that matter and wild life (the "serpent", the "wilderness", monkeys, for example) is often imbued with evil.

Consider other effects of agriculture on the mentality of mankind. Besides the notion of "harvest" it introduced two very important, closely related concepts into human affairs: "work" and "worth"—concepts that nowadays dominate all our lives.

Every clerk up from the suburbs to spend his day

entering figures in a ledger, every fitter, shop assistant, or draughtsman working his stint, is living in the shadow of those Neolithic pioneers who found that if they did not tend their fields regularly the weeds would choke the crop. We need not doubt that their huntsman predecessor had chores to do, and invented routines for passing the day. But how could he have distinguished between "work", which was like our leisure, and "leisure" that was like our work? The idea of repetitive application of most of the daylight hours to a schedule determined by human policies, whose neglect would be disastrous—this surely arose from agriculture.

If agriculture itself made possible a great explosion of the human population, this by-product, the concept of work, was a great accelerator of human organization and skills. A man could get out of working in the fields if he was doing something else that was useful—making tools, trading with neighbouring settlements, building houses, or computing when the river would flood again. But the standard of behaviour was set by the workers in the fields.

As the *Book of Proverbs* says: "Go to the ant, thou sluggard: consider her ways and be wise." If you were a non-farmer, you had not only to work but be seen to be working. Parkinson's Law began to operate: work expanded to fill the time available for it. And although much of it probably went in mere show of work or elaborate procedures, the abler men would direct their energies creatively. And as populations grew and became more tightly knit, men of vision could organize the work of many of their fellows in collective enterprises to build temples, canals, fortifications, and other great works whose traces persist to this day. Agriculture and civilization succeeded, and the ephemeral culture of the Palaeolithic years was replaced by industry of durable results. Further great inventions followed: wine, iron, paper, ships, sluices, pumps, clocks. But we should not overstate the pay-off.

It was fine for the men of vision, if they had the power, but for the common man the age of drudgery had begun, and has persisted to this day. His labour went unrewarded for thousands of years, because the wealth he created was sufficient to provide comfort only for a fortunate minority. In Europe and North America he had to wait until the technology of the twentieth century multiplied his productivity to give him a fair return. His brothers in most of the rest of the world are still working and waiting.

To keep up the morale of the workers through all the intervening centuries, men have had to brainwash one another with the virtues of work. Indoctrination in the nursery, in school, in church, in legend and literature, in casual conversation, has built up this almost unshakeable belief in work as something supremely virtuous and dignifying. Intelligent men of conscience brainwash themselves anew in each generation: they are aware, when they eat, of the labour that provided it and feel obliged not to spare themselves in their own occupations. They, too, are haunted by the Neolithic man with the hoe. As for the ordinary wage-earner, he is obsessed about his "right to work" and full employment, even when the state will pay him for not working. Without work he is afraid not so much of being worse off as of being somehow unmanned. He will throw out his chest with pride to say he is a collier, or a stoker, or a clerk or something else more to be pitied than admired, and although his job may be crucifying his body or his mind his worst fear is that he might lose it. He does not grudge the rich their riches, only their apparent idleness. The royalty which has survived in odd countries here and there comprises those who have worked hard at being royal.

Part of the myth has been the idea that hard work leads to great rewards. In the *Book of Proverbs* again: "In all labour there is profit." It is a myth easily sustained because, at the rudimentary level, if a man does not work he will be hard up and if he works overtime he will have more to spend. But such consequences of routine work are marginal compared with the enormous disparities in wealth which exist; and there are effective sanctions only because the common man customarily lives close to the margin. No, the individual escapes from the common drudgery by good fortune, in the form of inheritance, talent, cunning, or sheer luck. The hard work of a hundred generations failed to give any profit beyond mere survival to the population at large. It was then cunningly applied to the large-scale generation of wealth by a handful of scientists, engineers, and industrialists. But having thus broken through the prosperity barrier, we must prepare for the consequences.

Indeed, it is timely for us to realize, in the 1960s, that work was an invention, which can be dated to the invention of agriculture, because now, with the beginning of automation, we have to anticipate a time when we must disinvent work and rid our minds of the inculcated habit. As Dennis Gabor has written (*Inventing the Future*, London, Secker & Warburg, 1963):

For the first time in history we are now faced with the possibility of a world in which only a minority need work, to keep the great majority in idle luxury. Soon the minority which has to work for the rest may be so small that it could be entirely recruited from the most gifted part of the population. The rest will be socially useless by the standards of our present-day civilization, founded on the Gospel of Work.

I find it comforting to believe that Palaeolithic man was able to do without such a notion and that the universal confidence trick which the rich have worked on the poor throughout recorded history may soon become entirely obsolete.

Another all-pervasive notion arising from agriculture is "worth". The rough equation of labour and produce in the fields provided the basis for putting a value on things and on people, in the barter of food for artefacts and the payment of wages.

A man was to be rated not by his strength or by his skill but by his possessions; and it did not matter much how you acquired them, so long as you could retain them and pass them on to your children. Ingenuity of hand or brain was rewarded but such skills were, as they still are, "on tap but not on top". As the author of *Ecclesiasticus* observes:

> So every carpenter and workmaster that laboureth night and day; and they that cut and grave seals . . . the smith also sitting by the anvil . . . the potter sitting at his work . . . all these trust to their hands and every one is wise in his work. Without these cannot a city be inhabited. . . . They shall not be sought for in public council nor sit high in the congregation . . . but they will maintain the state of the world, and their desire is in the work of their craft.

A conscious or intuitive sense of the effect of supply and demand on the worth of food led on to the use of rather rare metals as tokens of value, and so the supply of grain and the stockpiles of gold have been the chief parameters of economic activity down to the present day. At first hand, preoccupied as we all are with taxes, grocery bills, and the like, the concept of worth seems supremely important. But on the broad scale it must all average out. Most of us will get roughly our *pro rata* share of the nation's goods and services; a few will manipulate the system to get a good deal more; and the taxes merely represent goods and services which we have whether we want them or not.

In these observations I am not denying the day-to-day convenience of money or dismissing the role of capital in constructive undertakings. All I want to recall is that our economic system is literally archaic, originating with agriculture, and describing a situation more than affecting it. This sceptical view of money is particularly necessary at a time like the present when what men can do is limited much more by available liquid assets than by ideas and technical skills.

The most obvious example is that the aid Britain and the USA give to the under-developed countries is limited, not by their productive resources but by the amount of gold in their vaults. If they are too generous, they will be held to be undermining the pound or the dollar. The result is that productive resources in developed countries can be under-employed because the system inhibits the nations concerned from even giving away their products to the needy.

With "worth" as with "work", I think our ideas are going to change radically in the foreseeable future. There is a variety of reasons, and one reason is variety. As more and more things have to be compared in value, the assessments become less and less real. While a crude computation may suggest that a haircut is worth an hour's wages or a house is about half as valuable as food for the family, such calculations are hardly possible in respect of pop records, sailing dinghies, or dish-washing machines. The result is that such things can be sold in large quantities at whatever prices the public seems prepared to pay.

Secondly, as productivity increases in the developed countries, something must give way. The obligation on the consumer to consume more and more, in order to keep the wheels of industry turning, is not particularly hard on the consumer, but it represents a tremendous waste of effort and is, in effect, making a nonsense of any evaluation of "worth". If the community is held to be better off because an individual scraps last year's model and buys a new one, then the value of the old one is *negative*; it is worth more scrapped than in running order. Of course, food producers have known this principle for a long time and have often increased the value of their crops by destroying or concealing part of them. What is new is the perennial rather than occasional use of such devices.

In a very practical sense, a ton of oil untapped underground may be more valuable than a ton of oil in a tanker, because it is confidence in the existence of reserves that makes possible present investment in aircraft, cars, power stations, and chemical works. Similarly, whatever the present market price of whaling products may be, the true cost is far higher because the whales are being extinguished by overkilling, and whalers are robbing future generations of the option of hunting (or taming) them. We are going to have to develop a new sensitivity about inorganic and living resources; now that man can conceivably exhaust several key resources in the foreseeable future, we must stop assessing these resources by the simple tests of the market-place and consider them instead from the hunter's standpoint of subtle conservation.

Yet another challenge to our traditional ideas of "worth" comes from the huge growth of new human activities. As long as science was the modest occupation of a few eccentrics, who earned their keep if necessary by teaching, it raised no special problems. Even today, the applied research which goes into, say, the development of new drugs or high-speed aircraft, can be audited in accordance with conventional economic tests. But the same cannot be said for some expensive new activities such as radio astronomy, which requires huge steerable aerials simply to discover philosophically interesting facts about the nature of the universe. How much is it "worth" to discover what the fantastically powerful celestial objects called "quasi-stellar radio sources" or quasars are? Any hope that we may find something useful to us is exceedingly optimistic. Again, what about the huge expenditures now required to build machines for the high-energy physicists, capable of reducing matter to finer and finer shreds? Machines now on the drawing board may cost more than £100 million; yet no one can say that the knowledge they will yield will have any economic pay-off, or even give the answers for which they are designed.

And then there is the Moon race, with which I started this chapter. Many thousands of millions of dollars and roubles are going into this decidedly useless exercise, which represents a wholly new kind of activity for the human race. In the last analysis, of course, politicians have to decide just how much they are prepared to spend on it, and thereby put a price tag on its "worth". But here, as for the expensive things in science proper, the decision is largely arbitrary. As basic economic problems recede in the wealthy countries, the instincts of the hunter begin to reassert themselves in defiance of cautious accountancy.

Thus, in spite of all the brainwashing, man remains mentally and physically a hunter, although it is part of our conditioning that we ignore or even abhor this notion. In fact, of course, it is far more dangerous to pretend that we are not predatory animals by birth than to admit that there is no reasonable hope that our nature will change in the foreseeable future. The evidence of a little introspection is so overwhelming that it seems almost superfluous to give instances, but when the obvious is overlooked one has to labour it a little. In conclusion, therefore, let me list some of our more obvious characteristics:

(1) Our anatomy, senses, and reflexes are those of an animal adapted to finding and striking. Only the fact that, unarmed, our teeth and hands are unimpressive disguises our true character that brackets us with the lion and the wolf.

(2) Our curiosity and our exploratory behaviour, and the powers of observation and induction on which modern science is based, are plainly well adapted to the purposes of tracking, anticipating, and outwitting other animals.

(3) Our greatest ingenuity has consistently been applied, not to the gentle arts of agriculture, but first to hunting and then to exploration and war; no farmer ever won the honours which are bestowed upon soldiers and spacemen.

(4) Our recreations—with the notable exception of gardening—are largely based upon situations of contrived unpredictability and tension, with an element of mental or physical skill thrown in, which owe much more to the chase than to the routines of agriculture. What is true of chess or classical drama is equally true of football pools, bowling alleys, or driving fast cars, even of some people's sexual behaviour. Those who are rich enough simply go hunting.

CHAPTER 3

Growing More Food

As THERE are dozens of ways of producing more food, there is no technical reason why agriculture should not in principle expand to give adequate diets for the rising populations of the under-developed world. Some of these possibilities are explored in this chapter. But if the technical obstacles are slight, far more formidable ones confront us in the forms of poverty, illiteracy, and unsuitable institutions. The cost of bringing about the necessary expansion in agriculture in the remaining decades of the century will be very high, in terms of capital investment. But it will also be high in another sense—the loss of land and its natural inhabitants—if much of the increase is brought about by erecting new fences and enlarging the area of farmland, rather than by increasing the yields from each acre of land already under cultivation. In settling on strategies for bringing about the increase, the aim must be to minimize the cost in all senses.

Because the technical possibilities sound so grand, it is perhaps as well to say something about the human and social problems before beginning our biotechnical excursion.

The way leaders in the under-developed countries have tended to turn their backs on agriculture has been mentioned in Chapter 1, but even when the will is there it may be economically very difficult for them to do much about it. The same helplessness prevails among the small farmers of the poorer countries. Hard work is no remedy: the land is, by and large, giving as much as unaided toil can procure and, if anything, there are too many people working on the land as it is. Better techniques, and the money to pay for them, are essential. But, where the economics of the market place prevail, the general population must be wealthy enough to buy more food, if the farmers are to be able to afford to produce it.

This implied vicious circle can probably be broken by authoritarian methods, as the Chinese are attempting; but in a democratic "mixed" economy the task may often be impossible without help from outside. Indeed, the crucial political test of the twentieth century is simply this: whether democratic institutions can cope with world poverty. On present showing, they cannot. But they could do so, better than the authoritarian régimes, if the prosperous democracies would play their part. I do not mean by this that aid for agriculture should be distributed according to political tests. It is rather that, given adequate aid and rising prosperity in all emergent countries, the fairness and opportunity for individual initiative that democracy makes possible in conditions of wealth and literacy will begin to take effect, and show superiority.

Yet indifference is not too strong a word to describe the present attitude of the well-fed countries, despite all the aid to the poorer countries (for agricultural purposes among others) disbursed by governments, and by the general public through Oxfam and the Freedom from Hunger Campaign. The scale and the institutional forms which such aid takes do not yet begin to match the problem. Hundreds of billions of dollars' worth of aid are going to have to flow in the next couple of decades if we are to avoid disaster. At present we are, as it were, trying to contain a forest fire with a few buckets of water.

And there is the awkward problem of conservatism in the poorer countries. This takes various forms, but the most important concerns the parcelling out of land. In some countries, near-feudal landlords exploit a depressed farming population for whom the rewards of effort are slight. In others, where land reform has been carried out, the break-up of estates into small peasant holdings, while socially equitable, is technically retrogressive because the technical and economic advantages of large-scale working are lost (herein lies the strength of the Chinese commune system). There are other forms of conservatism arising from ignorance, illiteracy, and superstition, which make it often very difficult to introduce new farming methods and new diets. The other side of this particular coin is that innovators are, very properly, unwilling to disrupt traditional ways of life without regard for human dislocations, which can range from technological unemployment to the loss of traditional moral codes.

FEEDING THE SOIL

One of the simplest methods of increasing food production is to use more fertilizer on the land. Every ton of ammonium sulphate added to the paddy fields of India produces an *extra* yield of two and a half tons of rice. As a ton of rice is worth about twice as much as a ton of ammonium sulphate the potential profitability is substantial. In ammonium sulphate the key chemical element is nitrogen; phosphorus and potassium are other elements widely used in fertilizers, where shortages of these elements set limits to agricultural production. In Australia dramatic improvements have followed the discovery that much land is deficient in other elements which are needed only in very small amounts—the so-called "trace elements".

Only when fertilizers are already used as heavily as in the Netherlands do the benefits of further additions become small; the scope for increasing yields by the use of fertilizers everywhere else—even in Britain—is immense. At present the land of the richer countries gets on average about ten times as much fertilizer as the land of poorer countries. It is only comparatively recently that European farmers have realized that it is well worth while putting fertilizer on grassland used for cattle and sheep.

World food production could probably be doubled by this one measure—use of fertilizers—alone, provided that attention were paid to the choice of crop varieties suited to the more fertile conditions. With other, parallel improvements in farming methods the gains could be greater still.

But, of course, to say that and to bring it about are very different matters. Accomplishment depends on capital investment in chemical plant and in transport services for taking the fertilizer to the farmers; it also requires that farmers be educated in its use and that they be helped financially to obtain it and to sell the food so produced at an economic price. These last requirements are stringent indeed, and can be fulfilled only by a general rise in prosperity of the poorer nations.

Phosphate and potash fertilizer has to be mined, but most of the nitrogen fertilizer comes from synthetic ammonia made chemically from nitrogen in the air, or from a by-product of the gas and coke industry. It is the phosphate that is probably most critical in the long run because a lot of nitrogen is regenerated in the soil by natural processes. Phosphate, however, tends to be drained from the soil at each harvest, and where (in India, for example) farms remain relatively rich in natural phosphate it is often a sign simply that productivity has always been low. There seems to be plenty of mineable phosphate rock dotted about the world, notably in the USA, USSR, China, North Africa, and some islands in the Pacific and Indian oceans.

Short of massive investment in fertilizer production—which will surely be necessary—there are other, older methods of encouraging soil fertility, of which the use of animal and human dung is an effective way of restoring nitrogen and potassium. Human dung, in particular, is wasted in most parts of the world except China and Japan. The rotation of crops, and in particular the use of legumes and grasses on fields from time to time to encourage the natural capture of nitrogen, is also of great value. This "fixation" of nitrogen from the air depends on the activities of microbes in the soil and in nodules in the roots of plants.

A technical hope of considerable interest, which is exercising research workers in several countries, is that we shall discover precisely how the nitrogen-fixing bacteria do the trick. The synthesis of ammonia in chemical plants, from the nitrogen of the air, is at present carried out at high temperature and high pressure, yet insignificant-seeming bacteria can accomplish nitrogen fixation on a cold English day from the unpressurized English air. As is usual with such natural processes, a complicated sequence of steps is involved, using tools of extreme subtlety: enzymes, very complicated protein molecules encouraging the reactions in question. It is by no means impossible, however, that our skills in microbiology and biochemistry will not only reveal completely how the natural process goes but will also enable us to mimic it in our industrial production of nitrogen fertilizers. If so, the cost of such fertilizers may fall abruptly and (what may be equally important) the chemical plant may be simple enough to be used locally in less-developed countries far away from the centres of sophisticated chemical engineering. It is, however, too early to say what the outcome of this line of research will be.

CONTROLLING WATER

Water control is another indispensable "input" in farming; both drought and flooding limit food production. Development of irrigation is closely tied to the use of fertilizers. Often the potential benefits of fertilizers cannot be realized because the land is parched; conversely, the cost of irrigation schemes may not be justified unless fertilizers are used to enlarge the yields from the irrigated land.

Irrigation is often thought of as being important only in arid areas of the world. Yet even in England, especially the south-east, it is often rewarding to water the land in summer. All the same, in Britain and most other countries of Europe, as well as in Japan and much of the United States, what is really more important is drainage.

"Watering the deserts" is one of the age-old ambitions of men; indeed the early civilizations arose in areas with little rainfall but watered by great rivers—in Mesopotamia and in the valleys of the Indus and the Nile. But from those times to the present men have made huge errors in spreading water without adequate drainage, so that the ground becomes water-logged or salty—or both. Just as salt in the fields probably destroyed the pioneer cities of Sumeria, in our time salt and waterlogging are still grievous problems, notably in modern West Pakistan where more than half the land irrigated by the Indus is affected; at one stage the damage was spreading at a rate of about 200 acres a day and an area larger than East Anglia had been thrown out of production.

The yields from the desert lands watered by the great rivers could be greatly increased by proper use of fertilizers combined with shrewder use of water; yet in the traditional irrigated areas the rivers are already heavily committed. Perhaps the greatest opportunities for bringing vast arid and semi-arid areas under cultivation are in the Soviet Union and, possibly, in China.

The Aswan High Dam, rising to make the sacred Nile pause in its course, is one of the most striking of present schemes. The dam is intended to provide both irrigation and hydro-electric power for Egypt. It is creating a huge reservoir, flooding the valley (and, incidentally, many Nubian monuments) far into the Sudan. The promise is immense: 2,100 megawatts of power and two million acres of newly watered land. But there is also a sufficient string of questions attaching to the scheme to make it a suitable illustration of the kinds of snags which may occur, not necessarily in practice at Aswan but potentially there, and elsewhere.

There are nagging questions about the soundness of the water planning (hydrology) that has gone into it. How much of the Nile's water will evaporate from the reservoir into the dry desert air? How much will seep into the underlying rocks and be lost? Will the irrigation scheme raise the level of underground water and bring deadly salt to the surface, as has happened in so many other places? How quickly will the silt carried down by the Nile accumulate behind the dam, perhaps clogging it?

Other questions concern biological aspects. What will happen to the farms downstream of the dam, which have for millennia relied on an annual supply of the fertile silt, when the silt is stopped by the dam? Again, will the water behind the dam be invaded by alien weed, either the Brazilian water hyacinth which has spread to so many African rivers (including the Nile itself) or the silvania which threatened the dam at Kariba? Finally, there is the disease bilharzia which causes great suffering in many irrigated regions of the world; it is transmitted by water snails in the irrigation canals. What can be done to control it at Aswan?

These questions are by no means exclusive to Aswan, and it is probable that, on balance, the new dam will bring great benefits to Egypt. But they serve to remind us that building a dam is by no means as simple an act of kindness as it is often thought to be.

Yet man's control over rivers can be magnificent in its results. One thinks of the Tennessee Valley, of the taming of the Rhône by French engineers, of the ambitious plans for the Mekong Valley in Indochina which have been worked out by computer, of dozens of big and little schemes all over the world. And one thinks too of the astonishing Soviet idea for diverting the Rivers Ob and Irtysh from their natural course to the Arctic Ocean, into the dry land to the east and south of the Urals.

But there are definite limits to the available supplies of

natural fresh water. It is for this reason that UNESCO has organized the International Hydrological Decade, 1965–74, to make a better inventory of surface and underground water supplies, and to train people who can devise sounder ways of using what is available, bearing in mind the demands not only of agriculture but of industries and cities too.

Beyond this search, there are two radically new possibilities for increasing the supply of water. One is the desalination of sea water; the other is modification of the climate.

Already desalination is providing drinking water for a few communities—in the United States and in the British Channel Islands for example—but no technique is yet economic for large-scale use in irrigation. The greatest hopes at present attach to an evaporation method ("flash distillation") using waste heat from huge nuclear power stations—but this only makes sense if you also need the huge power output. For poorer countries we still need the improvement of the basic methods, perhaps by devising better membranes for "capturing" the salt ions dissolved in the water; or the invention of a new principle which might conceivably emerge from the new interest in the fundamental physics of liquids.

CHANGING THE CLIMATE

With an eye to irrigation and farming in the semi-arid regions of the world, we have to pay close attention to those small changes that seem to be occurring in the world's climate (for example, making the Middle East drier and West Africa wetter), which may be critical in their effects on the summer rainfall on which the farmer depends.

Recent long droughts, and the consequent need for famine relief in various parts of the world, have provided a sharp reminder of how precarious farming is in places of low rainfall. An occasional bad year may be endurable, but two or three in quick succession can wreck the agrarian economy of a semi-arid country.

The whole question of water supply for agriculture is intimately tied up with weather and climate. For most of the time that life has existed on Earth, the world climate has been warm and balmy, with the poles free from ice and the sea-level high. Men came on to the stage at an almost unique time; we occupy much of our land—notably in the river plains that cradled our civilizations and still support most of the human race—only by virtue of the locking up of so much water in the ice caps and glaciers, the remnants of the most recent in the series of "freeze-ups" that we call the ice ages. Ice rules our present climate; by maintaining a marked difference in temperature between the poles and the equator it promotes that turbulence in the atmosphere which gives us the stormy changeable weather of the present era.

Moreover, living at the time of the passing of an ice age we can detect long-term fluctuations in the climate. For example, the Sahara has advanced northwards (and not only by human agency) since prehistoric men hunted in forests and left their cave drawings where now the desert broods; even in Britain there have been several perceptible changes of climate since Roman times, which have had their effect on farming. On a time-scale of many thousands of years the ice is retreating, though there have been resurgences of cold such as the "little ice age" of medieval times. As far as climatologists can make out from statistical studies, we seem now to have passed the end of a half-century of overall warming and have the prospect of a different climate in the century ahead. The possible changes, already mentioned, in the climate of the Middle East and parts of Africa could have profound effects on plans for economic development.

It is an awesome prospect that man himself may soon be able to affect the climate on a global scale. There can be no doubt, of course, that his extension of agriculture over the face of the Earth has had some effect already on local climates; nor is there much doubt that by engineering works, such as the blasting of wind-passes through mountain ranges to admit moist air into desert regions, or damming some of the narrow straits through which warm or cold ocean waters flow, significant regional changes could be deliberately brought about. But worldwide effects are also conceivable now. We can see the possible means only sketchily; we can see the consequences of such actions even less clearly because our knowledge of how the engine of the atmosphere works to produce our present weather and climate is too rudimentary to allow us to trust any meteorologist with predicting the outcome of a given large-scale experiment.

We can at least say that there are vulnerable points in the system where human interference could have profound effects—leaving aside for the moment the question of whether these effects would be good or bad. A former head of research of the US Weather Bureau, the late Dr Harry Wexler, suggested that the detonation of a number of H-bombs in the Arctic might set up a self-sustaining ice cloud that would have the effect of warming the whole polar zone; it could, he warned, start another ice age by increasing snowfall in the sub-Arctic regions. Again, the rarified layers of the upper atmosphere have an effect on the weather lower down out of all proportion to the amount of matter they contain, because they regulate the passage of radiation from the Sun and out again from the Earth; it is fully possible that the dispersal of quite small amounts of chosen vapours could alter the heat budget of the Earth. Another set of possibilities arises if we imagine almost unlimited sources of energy available to man—as might come, for example, from the development of "power from sea water" by means of hydrogen fusion reactors (see Chapter 4). The sheer growth in man-made energy might have a perceptible warming effect. Alternatively, power might be used for pumping cold, low-lying ocean water to the surface over a large area.

Nevertheless, the natural instabilities of climate lead us to suppose that such options in artificial climate change will soon be open to men that they may substantially alter the map of the world. They will also run into a new series of international disputes provoked by climatic experiments or climatic miscarriage. It may be that if, in the long run, men's lives become more directed towards the sea the decision may be taken to melt the ice, drown our present cities, and float on the raised balmy waters of a "normal" earth. But that is surely far off; in the short run we can expect greater success in weather control—dispersal of fog and hail, making rain fall in chosen locations and perhaps even cooling off hurricanes; and local climate control, particularly perhaps with a view to admitting moist air through the mountain barriers of the Californian and Gobi deserts or creating artificial seas, for example in the Qattara depression of the Western Desert.

We may be sceptical about the likelihood of global climate control for a very long time—not because it is too difficult but because small changes are likely to annoy as many people as they please; as for large changes, no one is likely to favour a return to the ice age, while an approach to the world's "normal" ice-free climate could be undertaken only if we were prepared to see the submersion of nearly all our existing centres of civilization, and a huge reduction in the area of habitable land.

POISONING THE "PESTS"

Greater controversy today surrounds another of the principal methods of increasing food production—chemical warfare against insects and other pests. The late Rachel Carson's *Silent Spring* prompted much heart-searching even among her fiercest critics, because of the attention that she drew to the possible effects of pesticides on species other than those against which they were directed. In the chlorinated hydrocarbons, of which DDT and BHC are the prototypes, we have very effective weapons against insects. Their advantage over natural insecticides such as that which comes from the pyrethrum flower is in their persistence; they continue to be effective long after they have been sprayed or dusted on wall, soil, or seed. This very persistence increases the risk that they will have indiscriminate effects. Nevertheless, in tropical medicine they save many lives from insect-borne disease, and in agriculture they can be of immense value. At least a third of the world's production of food is probably lost to insect pests.

While there is chronic attack by insects on many crops from year to year, keeping down yields, there are also disastrous outbreaks which bring ruin to the afflicted farmers. For example, in 1961–2 there was a terrible attack by leafworm on the Egyptian cotton crop; the use of DDT brought it under control. The most spectacular pest of all is the locust, which has haunted man since Biblical times. Now it begins to look as if the locust may be practically beaten, thanks to international action, to careful scientific study of the conditions in which locusts swarm, and to shrewd use of chemical pesticides (aided in part by the cannibalism of locusts, so that one poisoned locust kills others). This accomplishment alone, if the years ahead confirm it, should add 10 per cent or more to the total production of food in the world.

Alarm about abuses of chemical agents cannot be allowed to stand in the way of their essential contribution to increasing food supplies; in the final judgement, the life of a man must be rated more important than the life of a pigeon. The controversy has, however, served three very important purposes. It has had some effect in preventing gross misuse and careless handling of pesticides on the part of farmers, who may be beginning to realize that the poisons they use are indeed poisons. Secondly, it has stimulated the biologists and chemists to look again at methods of pest control. The biologists are now demanding, perhaps belatedly, that the use of chemical pesticides should be discriminating and controlled, with a careful study of the balance between pests and their natural enemies. For example, a sudden decline in a pest on which another species feeds may starve out the latter while leaving the pest to recover; conversely, careful reduction in the level of a pest may bring it more firmly under the control of its natural predator. (One difficulty is that there do not seem to be enough biologists to station one in every district.) But other methods of pest control are also under development, which are intended to be much more specific in their effects—for example, attacking one pest while leaving other, often benign, species unharmed. Interfering with the sex life of insects has interesting possibilities—for example, releasing male flies that have been sterilized by radiation; or spreading the sex-attractant scents of female insects to confuse the males.

The third benefit of the alarm about pesticides is that it reminds us that agriculture is a war between man and nature, and that the intensification of food production by agricultural means can only sharpen the struggle. Regardless of arguments about the advantages or hazards of particular chemicals or methods in particular cases, the general situation is indisputable—that man can continue to feed himself by agriculture only by attacking the natural world yet more fiercely. Every tidy field is an affront against nature; every incursion by pests is an attempt to restore the untidy diversity that characterizes the natural world. When traps, scarecrows, and hoes were the chief defences of the farmer, the battle was scarcely remarked upon; now that poisons of extraordinary potency are available to him we see how ruthless he has to be. So those who have no wish to live in an entirely man-made world may actually find a little comfort in the awkward behaviour of those many insect sub-species that have emerged with resistance to DDT and other pesticides.

Chemical warfare is not directed only against animal pests. Weeds—that is to say, unwanted plants—have come under chemical attack which is proving even more effective. The agents concerned are based on the elucidation of natural processes controlling the growth of plants: interference with the natural control kills the weeds. These techniques are being perfected to the point where it may no longer be necessary to plough the land in order to keep weeds under control. The consequences for farming practice may be quite revolutionary and an end to ploughing may reduce desiccation and erosion of the soil. Perhaps farmers who are still using ineffective wooden ploughs will skip the Iron Age and go straight into the Chemical Age! While it is hard to estimate the numerical gain to world food production from the use of weed-killers, there can be little doubt that they help to provide a short cut to modern farming standards for primitive farmers—provided, as in the case of fertilizers, that the use of the chemicals can be suitably financed.

Ranking alongside insect pests and weeds as causes of loss in agriculture are the diseases of plants and animals. Wheat rust, powdery mildew of grapes, swine fever, foot-and-mouth disease—these and many others bring endless misery to farmers and steal food from the mouths of the hungry. In some cases, chemical agents or vaccines can provide protection, or new varieties of plants or animals can be bred showing greater resistance to the diseases. Often there is no obvious remedy, or else the disease can be fought only by elaborate and costly methods—such as those being tried against the disease of cattle akin to human sleeping-sickness, which is spread by the tsetse fly and which seals off much of Africa from the cattle farmer. Animal disease is a subject of immense importance, deserving more research than it attracts at present, because an improvement in the diet of most of the world's people depends upon a prodigious increase in the production of animal protein. The scrawny, sickly beasts that are so typical of tropical husbandry do not inspire much optimism.

Other natural enemies of the food producers include

the animals, moulds, and bacteria which attack stored food; here there are techniques of fumigation, refrigeration, dehydration, and packaging which, if applied universally, could improve net food supplies by at least 10 per cent, and some would say much more.

HARVESTING NEW SPECIES

One of the startling features of modern agriculture is that it is still based almost entirely on the rather small number of species of plants and animals domesticated thousands of years ago by the first farmers. Since then, man has been incredibly uninventive in extending the range. A corollary is that much effort in the under-developed countries is devoted to copying the agricultural methods of the advanced, temperate-zone countries, which may not be at all the best methods for them.

There is, of course, a fantastic range of plants and animals made available to us by the natural world. Among plants, we can be sure that if other genera secured the attention that existing crops have had, with an eye to domestication and improvement, all kinds of possibilities would emerge. One that has been so treated, with very impressive results, is the microscopic aquatic plant *Chlorella*, which can be grown in water tanks. For less extreme departures, from relatives of established crops (the wild grasses, for example), we should be able to select varieties especially suited to particular climatic conditions.

Among animals, some obvious candidates for new domestication include the ungulates—wildebeest, giraffe, antelope, zebra, etc.—of the African gamelands; and ostriches too, as a means of transport as well as a source of food. There is also the aquatic manatee, which grazes on water weed.

To digress for a moment from the needs of food production, we can think of taming monkeys to open up a quite new form of domestication: to do menial tasks that require a shadow of human intelligence and dexterity—for example, fruit gathering, simple tasks on a production line, washing up, room sweeping, and so on. Professor B. F. Skinner has proposed that birds might be used for the sake of their sharp visual perception; for example, they could spot discoloured peas going past them on a conveyor and peck at a button to reject them.

But we can, and should, look at the possibilities of new sources of meat in a quite different way. Antelope and zebra are likely to be more viable than cattle of European stock in their gamelands, being better suited to the climate and resistant to local disease. They are also adapted to the natural grazing there. Thus one is led to a concept of protein for Africa which is the very antithesis of agricultural practice.

The gamelands of Africa, so the argument goes, represent in their balanced communities of wild plants and animals about the most productive use of the land that is conceivable, without enormous investment in modern agricultural methods. Except to the extent that it has been disturbed by man and recent changes of climate, here is nature's optimum "solution" for life in that part of the world. Moreover, the large animals are perfectly edible. Therefore the right approach is not to clear them off to make room for domesticated beasts but to let them be—in all their variety and magnificence—and to "crop" them. That is to say, they should be killed at just the rate, worked out by careful scientific study, which maintains them indefinitely in their most productive state. The yields will not be high by comparison with, say, European husbandry, but still good considering the difficult character of the country. Modest experiments along these lines have begun in Africa.

In noting these revolutionary possibilities, we should not lose sight of the almost unlimited opportunities for improving the existing plant crops and domestic animals. The huge differences in the yields per acre of, say, wheat in England, corn in the USA and rice in Japan, on the one hand, and the same crops in under-developed countries, are due at least as much to selection and breeding of improved varieties as to better farming methods. Plant breeders must take account of local conditions, and their successes in the advanced countries may be of limited applicability elsewhere. Even so, there are sufficient analogies in conditions between various regions for wholesale transplantation of improved varieties to suitable areas to be possible and desirable—with local increases in production of the order of 10 to 30 per cent as the likely reward. Yet the introduction of a crop into a new area, such as wheat into Northern Canada, has often depended on the evolution of a new variety. What is needed is a big effort in plant breeding in the tropics, developing special varieties for the whole range of crops.

The same is true of animal breeding. There is tantalizing evidence, for example, that cross-breeds of European and local cattle can give much better animals for subtropical and tropical conditions, but the effort in this direction so far has been small. Differences in yield are barely credible: an individual cow in Europe gives about ten times as much milk a year as one in the Indian sub-continent. Breeding is not all, but it counts for a lot.

Considering how simple and effective artificial insemination has become in the advanced countries it is intolerable that more is not being done elsewhere. Nor should we forget those rather despised domestic animals, the goat and the buffalo, which could, if taken seriously, play a much greater part in supplying milk and meat in the tropics.

A strong possibility of breeding essentially new kinds of plants and animals, from the existing species, arises from modern biology and the new-found ability to interfere radically with natural genetic mechanisms. By informed manipulation, one can, for example, overcome the barrier which prevents wheat from forming hybrids with other cereals. Less subtly, one can produce mutants by attacking the hereditary material in the genes with radiation or chemical agents; most of these mutants are not viable, but occasionally one may hope to find a new plant that is in some respects superior. These present activities are, however, as nothing when compared with what is promised by current research in molecular genetics. It is doubtful whether man will ever be able to carry out Frankenstein's programme of assembling a living organism from its constituents, except in the case of the simplest living things, viruses, which were first synthesized in a test-tube at the University of Illinois in 1965. But it will almost certainly become possible to blend or delete chosen portions of the hereditary information of existing plants and animals to create combinations of features—chimaeras—that have never existed on Earth before. Hard though it may be at this early stage to grasp the possible consequences, especially if such techniques should be applied to human genes, we can at least think it no longer entirely far-fetched to envisage, say, the development of hens with woolly coats, or cows that can chew and digest wood.

ASSESSING THE REGIONS

In his excellent and seminal study, *Possibilities for Increasing World Food Production* (FAO, 1963), Walter H. Pawley reviews not only the various techniques dealt with in this chapter but also the regional prospects by climate types. There are sharp differences of opinions between agronomists, soil scientists, and others about the possible enlargement of the area under cultivation, ranging from the view that three-tenths of the land can be regarded as cultivable to the conclusion that the area properly adapted to food production is less than what is now under cultivation. Adopting a fairly optimistic view, Pawley gives the following global estimates, here expressed in acres per head of the present world population (original figures in hectares per head):

Actually cultivated	1·1
Potentially useable	2·6
Inadequate soil	1·2
Too arid	2·5
Too mountainous	2·5
Too cold	2·5

There can be little real doubt that, in principle, great unused or under-employed tracts of the world could be developed as new food-producing areas. But we shall do well to remember not only the cost of such development but also the disasters that have overtaken attempts to transplant agricultural practice to land only marginally suited to it. Readers will recall the "dust bowl" in the USA in the 1930s, the ground-nuts fiasco in Tanganyika in the 1940s, and the more recent difficulties encountered by the Soviet "virgin lands" policy. We have to mark less spectacular but chronic soil erosion in many places around the world.

At the other extreme from the deserts, discussed earlier, are the luxuriant rain forests of the tropics, typified by the Congo and Amazon basins and the Malay Peninsula, where only small pockets of land have come under cultivation despite the heavy rainfall and high temperatures that promote biological abundance. Inaccessibility, disease, and the extreme vulnerability of the soil when the forest cover is removed are some of the chief impediments. Development in these areas will require a great investment in science and capital and will probably take the form of plantations of useful trees. Pawley suggests: "An agricultural revolution comparable to the opening up of the grass and forest lands of the temperate areas of North and South America and Australia lies somewhere ahead." I wonder.

On either side of the tropical forest belt are the savannahs characterized by wet and dry seasons. Only in Asia are they intensively farmed and by and large they are difficult regions on account of unreliable climate and poor soil. Nevertheless, in regions like the Sudan, the Orinoco basin, and northern Australia, a shrewd choice of crops and agricultural methods could lead to a great increase in cultivation, in contrast with their present under-employment (by intensive standards) in cattle ranching.

In the northern hemisphere the well-watered temperate lands are already exploited very fully; but the corresponding regions in Australia and South America have remained grazing areas. Now that the Australians have discovered deficiencies of nitrogen and key trace elements in their soils, the usefulness of their land should be greatly increased. The same may be true in Uruguay.

In the north, the Scandinavians have had some success in cultivating small parcels of land in high latitudes; and in northern Canada and Russia there is interest in the possibility of pushing agriculture northwards. Pawley doubts whether this will offer the world any large proportion of the benefit to be gained by bringing the tropics under domination; it requires not only a heavy initial investment to prepare the land for cultivation but also a heavy continuous use of labour, fertilizers, and forage crops. My own expectation is that people living in the far north will prefer to build huge domes as greenhouses for horticulture. But who will be living there?

Here, as in other regions, we cannot separate prospects for agricultural development from questions of where people will choose to settle. Apart from scientific, military, or tourist attractions, little is likely to draw men into the Arctic or Antarctic except the quest for furs and for minerals. The Russians and Canadians are engaged in careful geological surveys of their Arctic territories. The Canadians have found uranium and oil in the far north. Beneath the ice caps of Greenland and Antarctica there may be important mineral deposits, but they are going to take a lot of finding. True, research scientists can live at the South Pole in comparative comfort, and the trans-polar routes have been opened up by aircraft, nuclear submarines, and snow tractors; great works may indeed be undertaken in the polar regions. Yet in the global picture of human settlement, these areas are likely to remain fairly unimportant, at least in the foreseeable future.

Men evolved in a warm climate, but have already occupied all latitudes except the very highest. The quest for game, cultivable land, water and minerals and trade, has imposed the present pattern of economic and political geography. Men have carried their climate with them, in the form of clothing, buildings, heating, and now, for revolutionary development of the hot regions, air-conditioning. With increasing industrialization and better transport, neither the location of minerals nor proximity to farmlands need determine where those people live who represent an increasing part of human activity—clerical, scientific, and light industrial. Location becomes relatively unimportant. There is no technical reason why a semi-conductor factory should not be set up at a Saharan oasis, or a Government office in the highlands of Scotland.

The quest for pleasant surroundings and for comfortable or stimulating climates intensifies as transport and communications make it a more reasonable ambition. The inhabitants of the north temperate zone show every inclination to move towards the sun, whether to California, Florida, the Côte d'Azur, or the Crimea—and not only for holidays but to live and work as well.

A pattern for the future may well be this: increased technical domination of the areas towards the poles by a relatively small part of the human race, but for the majority slow migration towards the tropical, sub-tropical, and warm temperate zones (45° N to 45° S, say). Technical developments in disease control, in desalination of water, in nuclear power, and in air-conditioning will all reinforce this tendency. If occupation of regions such as Britain is to continue, where the climate is cool or variable, we may be confident that city-dwellers will demand that techniques such as the construction of domes (essential to make the Arctic more congenial) should also be applied for comfort and economy in these higher latitudes of the temperate zone. R. Buckminster Fuller's proposal for the

construction of a great dome over New York City is not
really far-fetched.

And what about the high mountains? In Pawley's table
(page 73) the amount of land considered too mountainous
for cultivation is more than twice as great in area as all
the existing farmland of the world. We may take the
agricultural limitations for granted but still ask whether
we cannot make mountains habitable and, by the same
process, suitable for horticulture in greenhouses. The
chief questions are those of transport, cold, and lack of
oxygen. There is no special difficulty in providing transport by rack railway or ropeway for tourists, skiers, and
astronomers; vertical-take-off aircraft, hovercraft, and
maybe even airships might be applied to the mountain
transport problem if anyone thought it worth bothering
about. As for the cold, there are plenty of mountainous
areas no colder than northern Europe. And while the
inhabitants of Mexico City live cheerfully enough in the
reduced oxygen at 7,500 feet, there would be no particular
difficulty in building pressurized homes and factories for
mountain dwellers just as we build pressurized passenger
aircraft. If the search for stimulating surroundings is one
of the factors in present human migrations we can reasonably expect the special charms of mountains to induce
people to look at these possibilities more seriously. There
are some countries, notably Chile, Peru, Equador, Tibet,
Switzerland, Austria, and the Balkans where mountains
occupy so much of their territory that serious utilization
of high terrain by modern techniques could radically
change the national way of life.

The edges of the land masses undergo slow change as a
result of erosion and sedimentation. The Dutch have gone
to great pains to enlarge the agricultural land area of the

world by building their polders. There are other coastal swamps that could be drained, but this may not be the only course. In the Gulf of Venice the Italians prefer to keep their shallows under water and promote fish-farming instead. Nevertheless, the real margins of continents are not their coastlines but the edges of their continental shelves, which commonly stretch a hundred miles or more offshore and provide a no-man's-land between the true geological oceans and the land.

FARMING THE OCEANS

I have deliberately left the oceans almost until last simply because it is here that the opportunities for cultivation of "natural" food supplies are greatest. It would be possible to replace land-based agriculture entirely by "aquiculture" of the oceans, and produce plenty for all. Indeed the trend of the argument in this book, which envisages the eventual reduction of agriculture by synthetic production of food (see Chapter 6) could also be sustained, on technical grounds, by the proposition of turning mainly to the oceans instead. For reasons that will become clear, I do not believe this is a good idea.

That the oceans can make a big and rapid contribution to immediate food supplies is beyond dispute. A recent demonstration has been the extraordinary development of the fisheries of Peru, taking that country from one of the least significant of fishing nations to a world leader. The anchovies off the west coast of Latin America were suddenly "discovered" by enterprising Peruvians as a source of animal food, and something like a gold rush began, increasing the catch one-hundredfold within eight years. Such an event should not surprise us, because we know that so far the undersea has been explored only indifferently from the point of view of fisheries. The oceans are vast, covering three-quarters of the Earth's surface, and the biological activity within them is correspondingly great. Although for some nations, notably Japan, the fisheries are of immense importance as a source of protein, all the oceans of the world supply no more food for man (in calories) than do the fields of Britain.

The supply could be at least doubled, perhaps increased by vastly more, by working along conventional lines. Thus, there are several measures that can greatly accelerate the growth of fish catches, all of which are being pressed by the Food and Agriculture Organization. These include educating the public in under-developed countries to eat more fish, or uncustomary species of fish, or fish flour; developing storage and processing facilities; fitting motors into sailing boats; and international management to prevent overfishing.

We could take it all very much further, by farming the sea. That means "sowing" selected species of plants and fish in selected areas. It means rearing young fish in tanks to protect them from natural hazards, and then releasing them. In certain suitable places—particularly in fjords and similar inlets—the sea can benefit from the use of fertilizers. We can "mow" the phytoplankton—the microscopic green plants of the sea—for feeding to animals or husbanded fish. Other possibilities include the coralling and shepherding of fish, the domestication of whales and dolphins, and the selective breeding of new varieties. We can even envisage the establishment of floating cities of fish-farmers and of underwater villages where divers live and work on the sea-bed.

But there is another side to it. For efficient sea-farming we should have to behave like the land-farmers, setting up fences and eradicating pests like starfish and squid from our domains. To the extent that we were successful, we would be repeating the conquest of the land, in the one really large, biologically interesting portion of the Earth that remains in a wild state. If disastrous mistakes are to be avoided, marine ecologists will have to make careful and prolonged study of the interactions of plants, animals, and the physical environment before any large-scale ventures beyond the present concepts of fishing are attempted. There are also very tricky questions of international law concerning the exploitation of the sea and the sea-bed. Precipitate action there cannot be. Accordingly, I do not see in sea-farming a particularly quick means of boosting world food supplies.

Yet men are turning increasingly to the undersea. In their diving masks and bathyscaphes they are drawn by science, by archaeology and sunken treasure, by the search for minerals, and by the sense of adventure, as well as by thoughts of new food supplies. Eventually, enormous numbers of people may live for much of their lives on or under the sea. I believe they will find a fascinating new way of life there. But I hope it will not be as sea-farmers. Let us regard the sea primarily as a three-dimensional living-ground, giving us more of that space which we shall need if our growing numbers are not to oppress us beyond endurance.

SEEKING A STRATEGY

There is, in any case, a fundamental objection to the idea that either exploitation of the oceans or synthetic food production can help the needy people of the world. It is that, for most of the under-developed countries, agriculture is the principal source of wealth, and the development of the national economy is inevitably tied to the prosperity or poverty of the rural economy. These nations, so the argument goes, must build on what they have, and the chief item in their inventory is the cultivated field. To quote again from Dr B. R. Sen, Director-General of FAO (this time from a statement to the UN Population Commission, March 1965):

It is an encouraging sign of the times that the role of agriculture in economic development is coming to be recognized on an ever-increasing scale. That the key sector in economic development in the developing countries is agriculture is fortunately no longer treated as a heresy. In these countries, 60 to 85 per cent of the population live on the land and derive their livelihood from agriculture. Agriculture must provide adequate supplies of food for the whole population. It must supply raw materials and provide the base for industrialization. It is the main source of investment capital, foreign exchange and manpower. Agriculture must provide a market for the budding industries of developing economies and release labour for industry. Crash programmes of industrialization, however attractive politically to those who are understandably impatient for change, cannot meet all these basic conditions for economic growth unless they are also accompanied by an agricultural revolution. There is no conflict between agricultural development and industrialization; they must go hand in hand; but in developing countries it is agriculture that has to produce the leverage for economic growth.

While development and implementation of synthetic or other new methods of food production is proceeding, agriculture must continue to grow as rapidly as possible. Not until roughly the end of this century may one expect agriculture to reach its peak in scale and importance. But if, in the meantime, world development has not passed beyond this dependence on agriculture, the situation will indeed be black.

For all we hear about "the developing nations", "freedom from want", and "overseas aid", the fine phrases and the apparent bustle about world development vaporize in the glare of terrible facts. The rich nations of the world are getting richer very rapidly; the poor nations, with only a few exceptions, are making virtually no headway. The rate at which the gap is widening is illustrated by the observation of Barbara Ward that the *increase* in the national income of the United States in 1964 was equal to the *total* income of all the nations of Africa. The widening gap cannot be a source of friendship between men, especially when we notice the uncomfortable fact that the richest countries are, roughly speaking, those whose inhabitants have white skins, and the poor are coloured. There are many theories about racial discrimination; the objective evidence points mostly to a crude basis in economic convenience.

Science has an uncomfortable connection with the present material and political ascendancy of the Europeans. Before the development of oceanic navigation in Europe and the associated emergence of the methods of modern science, nearly all the practical discoveries and inventions on which Europe depended had been made in the Arab, Indian, and Chinese spheres. The enormous advantage conferred on Europeans by modern science,

with the acceleration of material progress which it provided, was unquestionably a decisive factor in the age of
imperialism. Even more uncomfortable is the fact that
today, consciously or unconsciously, science and technology are still being applied with far more vigour for the
benefit of the northern "white" nations than for the
southern "coloured" nations whose needs are plainly
greater and more pressing.

In 1964, I organized a series of articles in *New Scientist*
in which we asked a hundred experts in many branches
of learning and practical affairs to look ahead to "The
World in 1984". They responded for the most part with
gusto, albeit moderated by some reservations about the
virtues of the technological world we were creating; but
whenever the series came near to matters relating to world
development it was like encountering icebergs in the
warm sea of scientific optimism. In particular, Abdus
Salam, who is Chief Scientific Adviser to the President of
Pakistan, had this to say:

> I would like to live to regret my words but twenty years
> from now, I am positive, the less-developed world will
> be as hungry, as relatively undeveloped, and as des-
> perately poor, as today. And this, despite the fact that
> we know the world has enough resources—technical,
> scientific and material—to eliminate poverty, disease
> and early death, for the whole human race.

We may wish to see this forecast proved wrong, but no
one who has followed the fruitless struggles of the past
twenty years can deny that, as a prediction on the basis of
the evidence, it is all too credible.

Experience in Mexico and Israel, in particular, has
shown that food production on land can indeed be

increased by a planned development programme. Education, research, irrigation, and expansion of the area under the plough have all contributed to a doubling of agricultural output in ten years in the case of Mexico, and a two and three-quarters increase in the case of Israel in the same period. There is encouragement in such achievement. But when we look at the world as a whole, and see food production barely keeping abreast of population growth, what are we to do?

There are certain inescapable facts that must govern our strategy. One is that nothing short of mass killing, by war, pestilence, or famine, will prevent the population from doubling by, roughly, the end of the century. Implementation of the most vigorous population policies in all countries is urgently necessary if we are to stabilize the population at perhaps three times the present numbers by the middle of the twenty-first century, but the more immediate prospect is that we can do little more than postpone by a few years the inevitable doubling. Those few years can make all the difference between prosperity and poverty, but that is a separate issue; meanwhile, we have to plan to feed twice as many people, and think about feeding three times. The population explosion is not a statistician's fancy, or an avertible disaster: it is a whole lot of hungry children.

Secondly, as we have seen, there is no single, magical solution to the immediate problem. Farming the sea and the synthetic production of food both represent long-term possibilities, but they could not be expected to make a major contribution to food supplies until about the end of the century. Rather, a great range of more-or-less established techniques has to be deployed to increase food production, along the lines indicated in this chapter, supplemented towards the end of the century by some of the novel ideas.

The third inescapable condition is somewhat paradoxical. The easiest way to increase food production is to put more effort into farming in the developed countries; but at the same time it is necessary to build up the rural economies of the under-developed countries and that is where the greatest effort must go. Nevertheless, the latter will plainly not be able to produce all the food they need, so the developed countries must increase their output and devise financial means of supplying this food to the poorer nations.

Finally, however we go about increasing food supplies, it is going to cost a very great deal of money, in the next thirty years, in the form of capital investment in fertilizer plant, irrigation and drainage schemes, training colleges, scientific research, and general improvements in farm practice. It will have to total some hundreds of billions of pounds, but at only a few pounds per head per annum it will be a reasonable price for insurance against hunger. We are neglecting to pay an adequate premium at present.

This question of financial cost, however, leads us back to the non-financial price that we shall have to pay. Another generation of farmers will have to slave in the fields. The war against "pests" and "weeds", meaning animals and plants that do not fit into the farmers' scheme, will have to be intensified and also extended, as new land is brought into production. Fences will enclose more of the Earth's surface. In many places wild life will be reduced to a few scavenging species. We shall make mistakes and probably destroy more soil.

It is not mandatory that we should try to minimize such consequences. If we can survive only by creating an exclusively man-made world we shall have to do so, although we had better be sure that we know precisely what we are doing or nature will hit back and crush our efforts. But I believe that the elimination of natural "enemies" or "obsolescent species" will leave the world intolerably poorer. Nor is it necessary, because the day is near when we shall be able to feed ourselves by quite different means.

Accordingly, our strategy for increasing agricultural output should be conceived with the aim of confining agriculture as closely as possible to its existing areas. It is necessary to take account of national boundaries and the right of each country to try to feed itself, and in Africa, in particular, we must expect the areas dedicated to food production to grow. In Asia, on the other hand, there is little scope for territorial expansion and better use of existing farmland is the supreme need.

There is an important qualification. "Watering the desert" and similar amelioration of extreme natural conditions can in principle extend the area available to many forms of life besides man. If we carry out developments of this kind with the idea that we are creating new gardens or parks, rather than with single-minded devotion to agriculture, we shall do well. Again, if we adopt the principle of game-cropping in the grasslands of Africa, we can, in effect, extend the effective area of food-production while preserving—possibly even improving—the conditions for wild life.

What we have to resist is the final assault of plough and pesticide on the remaining reservoirs of nature. If that were allowed, we might then as well leave the land for ever to the farmer, for all the pleasure it would give us. If we can prevent it, we can look forward to a time when we can knock down the fences, put away the spray guns, and try to recreate Eden.

CHAPTER 4

Means in Search of Ends

THE TECHNICAL options for enlarging food production, as outlined in the previous chapter, are only a small selection of the practical possibilities emerging from current science. This chapter will explore other aspects of knowledge and its applications. The purpose is to give an impression of the bustle of ideas amid which we are living and of the bewildering range of opportunities confronting us. Men are now able to do pretty well anything they put their minds to, within extremely wide though definite limits; that is the extraordinary consequence of their recent understanding of a relatively small part of the workings of the natural world. Unhappily, awareness of this power is still fragmentary and uncoordinated, and at present we have only opportunistic purposes for it.

There is good reason why there should be so little understanding of the substance and potentiality of science today. Half of what we know about the natural world has been discovered in the past thirty years (this assertion is tested in the table overleaf). In the face of this growth, there has been a near failure in communication.

Specialization separates the physicist from the biologist even before they leave school; by the time they become active research workers, the geophysicist and the high-energy physicist, or the field biologist and the molecular

A DOUBLING OF KNOWLEDGE

The proposition that scientific knowledge has doubled in thirty years can be tested by naming any discovery or invention of the period up to 1936, and seeking to match it by one of comparable importance in the period 1937–66. For brevity and emphasis this list concentrates on examples of major developments.

Up to 1936	1937–66
Discoveries	
Electromagnetic induction	Transistor effect
Distant galaxies	Quasars
Radioactivity	Nuclear fission
Atomic structure	Nuclear structure
Circulation of the blood	Mechanisms of photosynthesis
Electrical processes in nerves	Chemical processes in brain
Micro-organisms	Cell organelles
Theories	
Universal gravitation	*
Periodic table of elements	Symmetry theory of elementary particles
Theory of gases	Theory of liquids
Laws of thermodynamics	Invariance laws in high-energy physics
Theory of conductivity	Theory of superconductivity
Relativity	Non-conservation of parity, etc.
Quantum theory	Protein structure and mechanism
Evolution by natural selection	Heredity by genetic code
Inventions realized	
Steam engine	Electronic computer
Photography	Video-tape
High explosive	Nuclear explosive
Plastics	Antibiotics
Automobile	Hovercraft
Radio	Laser
Aircraft	Spacecraft

* It is hard to match Newton's great theory on a one-to-one basis, but it is no exaggeration to say that the cosmological implications of current astronomy and high-energy physics are comparable in aggregate.

biologist, are inhabiting separate worlds. For the general public, the science taught at school tends to stop in the nineteenth century; only the imperfect efforts of a tiny band of popular science writers serve to inform the public, and their administrators, about current developments. Only a very few people—some broadminded elder statesmen and administrators of science, some science writers, and the most avid of their readers—are privileged to study the majestic spectrum of present knowledge more or less in its entirety.

There is some regrouping within science which partially counter-balances the tendency to specialization. New fields of study like radio astronomy, medical physics, bio-engineering and so on bring together "multi-disciplinary teams" of people trained in quite different branches of science, though this effect is, in the first instance, a manifestation of the failure of the university departments to adapt quickly to the new lines of research.

The fragmentation of knowledge, blown apart among the minds of men by the explosive growth of our science, may not have been an unmitigated blight on the human intellect, although the mental divisions separating biologist from engineer, and both of them from the administrator, have prevented any one of them from grasping in full the astonishing powers that mankind has acquired, absent-mindedly and collectively, in its very recent past. For although, accordingly, the applications of science to everyday life have been slower than they might otherwise have been, at least no politician or military man has yet shown himself capable of exploiting the full repertoire of modern science for reasons of personal power.

But now there are urgent reasons for wishing to re-attain that synthesis of knowledge that came naturally to men of learning when there was much less to know. The piecemeal exploitation of technical opportunities cannot continue. Politicians have to seek to shape the world by explicit encouragement or disapproval of named innovations. Scientists who are faced with rationing their projects as they approach a ceiling in their expenditures need guidance as to what developments would be socially most desirable. (How can we compare the importance of neurophysiology, say, with nuclear physics? The answer does not lie in the domain of science.) And intelligent practitioners of the arts and "humanities" can no longer dodge their responsibility for understanding and commenting on the content and patterns of modern technology, by taking refuge in the vaguely anti-science attitude that has become so commonplace during the present century.

It is, of course, the emphasis on natural science in the inventory of human knowledge that antagonizes the non-scientists. The uncomfortable fact is that little which has not been acquired by the methods of science represents reliably cumulative knowledge. A humble physics graduate today can rightly claim to know incomparably more than Newton did; dare anyone affirm that in politics or international affairs we are to anything like the same extent wiser than the Romans, or in the arts and philosophy by so much superior to the Greeks? To ask that is not in any way to undervalue either worldly wisdom or poetry, but merely to suggest that, in studies of human affairs, the scientific revolution has still to happen. As we shall see in the next chapter, that revolution is not far off.

Meanwhile, it is appropriate to note the origins of our natural science. Before the seventeenth century, men had made a variety of useful discoveries and inventions—most notably in Asia. For reasons that will remain obscure and controversial until our historical methods are greatly improved, around 1600, in Europe, a series of actions by individuals and small groups of men set in motion the scientific revolution. The new "experimental philosophy" was embodied most enduringly in the Royal Society of London in 1661 and made articulate in its charter, in its motto (*Nullius in verba*), and in the actions of its early Fellows. The idea was an abstract one. It involved the substitution of observation for authority, of inductive for deductive reasoning, and the acceptance of objective experimentation as the final arbiter of all controversy between men of learning. It has proved to be the most important step in human affairs since the invention of agriculture. Just as agriculture made possible a sudden growth in the size and complexity of human communities, so the invention of modern science began an unprecedented enlargement of human knowledge and skills.

Science is a continuing process, rather than a collection of facts and theories, and a description of current knowledge is ephemeral (to the extent that reviews can be seriously out of date by the time they are printed) and also to some extent misleading because the emphasis must be on what we know rather than on what we don't know. But there is a large and securely interlocked framework of knowledge, enclosing virtually all known natural phenomena, which can be sketched by starting at any point and tracing some of the connections. Many of the details are unknown, and some of the main members of the framework are missing, but the structure stands. And depending on it are innumerable applications of this knowledge in human affairs. For present purposes, we can cavort on the framework to explore some of the more exciting possibilities, and in doing so we can conveniently note some aspects of established knowledge and a few of the more immediate trends.

INTELLIGENCE AND COSMIC EVOLUTION

Since the starting point is arbitrary, where better to begin than with the human species, and with the so far unanswered questions of whether we are unique in the universe or whether we shall be able one day to encounter other intelligent beings? On these questions several elements of current science and technology converge.

Communication with other intelligences could plainly be a turning-point in human affairs, exposing us to knowledge presumably much more advanced than ours and enabling us to know of civilizations utterly different in kind and concept from our own. At any rate it is now scientifically quite respectable to debate this possibility. The more we discover about the planets of the Sun's family the further our hopes decline of finding anyone else to talk to so close at hand. We can also calculate that men may never be able to travel far beyond our own solar system to visit the planets of other stars, because the rocket energy and time required appear to be simply impracticable. But advances in the techniques of signalling across large distances bring the compensation that we can think seriously about trying to establish links by radio or light, at least with the planets of the nearest stars—if such planets exist and if on any of them there are intelligent beings with the means and inclination to communicate.

The reconnaissance of Mars with television cameras in

Mariner IV in 1965 revealed a disappointingly barren-looking, Moon-like surface. If subsequent flights, in particular the landing of biological instruments—"life detectors"—on the Martian sands, reveal the presence of life, however primitive, that will provide good motive for starting a serious, continuous vigil with radio telescopes. They will probably be trained on the nearer stars, "tuned" to 21-cm wavelength, in the hope of detecting unnatural signals containing intelligence of some kind. On the other hand, if Mars is void of life or even of the kinds of chemicals associated with life, the expense of the vigil may not be justified.

Why is Mars so significant in this respect? Because the implication of current biology is that life is only a matter of chemistry and that it is plausible that wherever one has a planet with the right materials available at the right sort of temperature, life can appear spontaneously. Mars is, according to current observations, the planet of the solar system other than Earth most suitable for the appearance of life. Oxygen and water are in short supply but on general principles primitive life forms are possible. Discovery of them could be the most exciting outcome of the early decades of the space age, fraught with significance for fundamental biology in comparisons of the molecular systems adopted by life in radically different environments. It would also encourage the belief that other, more Earth-like planets of other stars are likely to support higher forms of life. If Mars is bare, we shall have reason to feel lonelier.

In speculating about alien intelligence one has to combine several imponderable factors: for the large number of stable, long-lived stars resembling the Sun, what is the likelihood of their having Earth-like planets, of life appearing on those planets, of intelligent life-forms existing on them now, of those life-forms being in a communicative frame of mind? For practical purposes, attention tends to focus on stars within a few tens of light-years of the Sun; that is to say, within reasonable signalling distance, such that signals take only a few tens of years to travel across the intervening space. Optimistically, one would like to be able to ask a question and get an answer within, say, a hundred years and we believe that no system of communication can be faster than light. Perhaps it is more reasonable to expect to pick up "broadcasts" from some of the much greater number of more distant planets, although in that case there can be no hope of a conversation within the human life span.

Many of the hundred thousand million stars in our galaxy, the Milky Way, may have intelligent life associated with them. If we assign reasonable numbers to the various probabilities we can persuade ourselves that there may be several such planets with communicative beings on them in orbit around stars lying within fifty light-years or so of us. They, in turn, may be in touch with other planets farther away, so that there may exist what Fred Hoyle has called a galactic telephone network and what I have called a Society of Eggheads of the Milky Way.

One has to assume that "they" will be trying to get in touch with us, guess how they are doing it, and simply listen out. The reason for thinking that 21 cm is the most likely wavelength is that it will be well known to all radio astronomers on all planets as the characteristic wavelength of hydrogen, the most abundant element in the universe. Before the end of this century, we may well have detected some sign or other of the existence of alien intelligences, but we can scarcely have begun a conversation.

Philip Morrison has suggested that if we succeed in making contact with more advanced communities scientific problems will divide themselves into two categories: those where answers can be expected from terrestrial research in less time than it takes to find out from the Eggheads, and those where it is probably quicker to ask them. In all this we may be grateful that even the more knowledgeable beings are unlikely to find interstellar travel a practical proposition, so we need not be unduly fearful about giving away the location of our planet to imperialistic Eggheads.

Behind much of the foregoing speculation about the evolution of intelligent life elsewhere is the broad explanation that modern science gives of how stars, planets, and living things came into being, from that raw material of the universe, hydrogen. Why the raw material should be hydrogen, with just its properties, is a question at the very heart of the problems of elementary particles of matter—problems that are currently exercising many of the world's leading physicists, in their theoretical researches and in their experiments with the giant "proton-smashing" machines.

Many of the details of the cosmic evolutionary processes are uncertain, unknown or unknowable, yet we can be confident, given hydrogen and plenty of time, that the mindless creation by nature of a world like the Earth with all its colour and life is entirely plausible.

First we have to have chemical elements other than hydrogen, and to do this nature begins by using the force of gravity to gather up hydrogen into dense clouds to make stars. At the high temperatures and pressures created by this process of condensation a nuclear reaction begins in which the hydrogen is built up into slightly heavier elements; in the process the stars come alight.

Then we have to sit back and wait for some thousands of millions of years until the star begins to run out of hydrogen. The steady burning comes to an end and, after some preliminary changes, the star explodes, creating in the space of a few minutes all the heavier elements known on Earth and some besides—elements heavier than uranium that are so unstable that they have not persisted in nature. Not all the elements occur in equal abundance: their quantities depend on the particular stabilities of the nuclei of their atoms. Some, like silicon, oxygen, carbon, and iron will later earn distinction by their commonness while others, like gold and krypton, will be remarkable for their rarity.

But we are anticipating. After the explosion of the "first generation" stars, these heavier chemical elements are but the merest taint in the pure hydrogen pervading space. To create a body resembling the Earth we have to distil most of the hydrogen away. So we need to create another star, this time the Sun, from a condensation of the now-contaminated gas, and we have to set lesser condensations of gas and dust in orbit round it—the proto-planets. Dust enters the picture because now the different chemical elements have a chance to react with one another: silicon combines with oxygen and other elements to make stone, and hydrogen combines with oxygen to make ice. As the Sun comes alight its rays energize the volatile hydrogen molecules of the nearer proto-planets, so that they escape their gravitational bonds. Thus the distillation occurs, leaving the inner planets as primarily stony spheres, the outer planets still retaining much more of their primeval hydrogen.

Now we have to single out the planet with most potential for further evolution: in the solar system it is the Earth, which is neither too close to the Sun nor too far away and where liquid water can persist for many aeons. At first it is a smooth sphere shrouded in an atmosphere of methane, ammonia, and water vapour. We have to put chemistry to work under the stimulation of the Sun's ultraviolet rays to make a soup in primeval water (probably lakes) from the reactions between the gases and the water—a soup containing complicated chemicals from which, after hundreds of millions of years of aimless experimentation, living things will evolve. At the same time we have to do something drastic about the face of the Earth if we are to prepare land for an eventual invasion by life and the development of higher forms. A smooth sphere uniformly covered by water would be fine for fish but not for men. Just why a quarter of the Earth's surface is quite different in nature from the ocean bed—why, in fact, continents exist at all—is a favourite subject for argument among Earth scientists, but volcanic action is as likely an explanation as any. Given the existence of a continental portion, geophysicists can see how natural forces break it up and shift it around by "continental drift" to produce the familiar map of the world; they can invoke the processes of mountain building and erosion, of sedimentation and ore formation, of earthquake and contemporary volcano, to complete the picture.

To return to our soup. By various stages we can suppose that blobs of chemicals will have appeared with hints of characters we associate with life: the ability to grow by feeding on the soup; the ability to divide to make similar blobs; the ability to use coloured materials to capture the energy of sunlight; and most important of all, an organization of the internal chemistry of a blob, giving it both immediate advantage over poorly organized blobs and the capacity to preserve its advantage for posterity by breaking up to form new blobs possessing similar properties. Not only do special molecules such as enzymes appear, with the capacity to accelerate certain chemical reactions with advantage to the blob possessing them, but master molecules such as nucleic acids come into service, able to sponsor the formation of enzymes. Furthermore, the organization within the blobs begins to assume the form of sets of enzymes and other molecules arranged like production lines.

A crucial invention is the machinery of photosynthesis, which uses light energy absorbed in pigments to combine carbon dioxide and water to make the "food" of primitive plants, and of all plants since. Life becomes much more productive and, what is just as important, photosynthesis releases oxygen to the atmosphere. The gradual build-up of oxygen over many millions of years alters the chemical environment of life and prepares the way for the subsequent invention of respiration, which makes life more "energetic". The oxygen also has two other effects of immense significance: it rules out any more "fresh starts" in life by "burning up" the vulnerable chemical precursors of novel organisms, and it draws a thickening veil of ozone (a form of oxygen) across the upper atmosphere to cut off the ultraviolet from the Sun. The ultraviolet has served its turn in driving the early chemical reactions preceding life; now its being cut off makes possible the eventual emergence of living things from beneath protective layers of water.

The creation by random processes and natural selection of primitive organisms is as complex and astonishing as the more familiar subsequent evolution from algae to men. Current investigations are showing how much more ancient are the molecular biological systems than are the species possessing them today, and we can think about retelling Darwin's great story of evolution in more exact, chemical terms. To give only a simple example, it turns out that many of the genes of widely differing species are indistinguishable, for the good reason that they are concerned with a common internal molecular organization rather than with the outwardly obvious characters. Here, in another form, is the reason for not seeking to create artificial organisms from scratch, as noted in Chapter 3.

Nevertheless, Darwinian evolution, through its succession of biological inventions and its invasions of the oceans and the land, up to the emergence of thinking men, remains at the core of all understanding of life. It teaches us the relationships between species and also sets the right value on living things. While they are not the product of special creation they represent the products of billions of years of painstaking trial and error—a blind alchemy turning the barren rock into the intricate living community of which we are a part. To present-day biological discoveries which find mechanistic interpretations of diverse processes, non-scientists sometimes react with distaste, as if the biologist in taking the mystery out of life were somehow diminishing it; on the contrary, he shows it in superb and chastening perspective.

This perspective of cosmic and terrestrial evolution suggests a range of startling possibilities open to men, at least in principle. Besides manipulation of the genes of plants and animals to produce new species, there is the purely scientific extension of present experiments on the origin of life to large-scale artificial environments where utterly strange life forms could be encouraged to originate. Deliberate or accidental modification of the Earth's atmosphere is also within our power, particularly at great heights where small quantities of materials can have a marked effect on the transparency of the atmosphere to various radiations from the Sun. Rocket exhaust might have such effects.

One day we may extend current research, aimed at simulating conditions in stars, to conditions equivalent to exploding stars, thereby producing fresh supplies of the rarer chemical elements. Meanwhile the Earth has only its cargo of atoms that have been battened down by gravity for thousands of millions of years. To be sure, there is some small loss of light gases from the top of the atmosphere, and a slow accretion of stony and iron meteorites—perhaps water too—gathered up by the Earth on its yearly orbit. But by far the greater part of the stuff of the Earth has been here since the beginning and in that time the material on the surface has undergone many metamorphoses in the natural dialectic of order and disorder, formation and decay. This being so, and with the prospect of quarrying other planets being far-fetched in a literal sense, we can see that at present the abundance of the elements on the surface of this planet sets limits to our practical possibilities.

NEW PHILOSOPHY OF ENGINEERING

Life on Earth and all the material works of men, then, are simply transformation of the available stuff in the environment, by means of energy dedicated to special functions. This is one of the great unifying ideas of current science: just as everything in the universe shares a common history, so everything on Earth takes part in a single drama, the chief actors of which are now those astonishing agglomerations of miscellaneous atoms and molecules we call men. This simple concept subsumes everything from rainfall to music, and draws its scientific strength from our abundant and growing knowledge of the physics and chemistry of the elements and of the transformations of energy.

Out of this knowledge comes a vast range of techniques, of course, and other remarkable opportunities for the future, to which I shall come shortly. Also it should be impressing on us a practical philosophy that makes us acutely conscious of our environment, in its material as well as in its aesthetic aspects. We are learning to take careful inventories of the ores, soils, and biological resources that we have been squandering. We are acquiring a bad conscience about the careless pollution of air and water with chemical and radioactive agents—so much so that today a great deal of scientific activity is devoted, very properly although negatively, to monitoring and mitigating the untoward side-effects of human activity. We see much of human disease as manifestations of environmentally induced disorders, linking dirt with infectious disease, overcrowding with mental and adrenal stress, and diet with heart disease. But just as health is more than the absence of disease, so a healthy attitude to environment is more than the avoidance of obvious error. It is the extension of scientific curiosity about the natural world to a sense of co-operation and conspiracy with nature in all our doings, so that not only do we understand much more deeply what our actions entail but we also find new pleasures in them. In adopting this attitude we shall find new, rational bases for our instincts and judgements.

In the same spirit we can judge the hitherto clumsy attempts to liberate the human body and brain from drudgery, by providing material wealth by machine. The industrial environment is typically ugly because, in developing new means of creating wealth, we have lost sight of its purposes and we have neglected even to adapt our machines to suit the men who have to work with them. But there is a new spirit in engineering which is going to change all that.

Under tags such as "ergonomics", "human engineering", or "man-machine interfaces", close attention is now being given to design that matches machines more precisely to the anatomy, physiology, and psychology of men. What is inescapable in designing a space-ship or a radar system is also being applied to automobiles, typewriters, and armchairs.

With the development of automatic machinery it similarly becomes necessary to define precisely the respective provinces of machines and of men. As a consequence, we begin to segregate what is routine and "boring" from those actions and decisions appropriate and "interesting" to men. Such is the pattern evident in the oil companies, which are among the most highly automated and computerized so far.

More profoundly still, the most advanced thinkers among engineers today are not content with devising machines according to someone else's specifications. The first question is not "what kind of bridge do you want?" but "why do you want to cross this river, anyway?". The second step is not to design a bridge but to analyse, from environmental, social, and economic viewpoints, the purpose the crossing is intended to serve, and to see what form of crossing—bridge, tunnel, ferry, etc.—may be

most appropriate, and what its effects will be. If, in the
end, a bridge is chosen, the new engineer is not satisfied
merely to improve a little on the last bridge he built, but
explores imaginatively (using computer-aided design
techniques) the very concept of a bridge, testing new
forms, materials, and methods of construction so that new
and aesthetically better compromises between cost and
purpose may be found. The first large-scale civil application of this engineering philosophy has been taking place
at the Massachusetts Institute of Technology in connection with Project Transport, aimed at devising new public
transport systems for the north-eastern United States.

Coming down to the modern equivalents of brass tacks,
it is in our production and use of materials of all kinds that
the atomic view of the stuff of the Earth is most explicit.
We can interpret their properties in terms of atoms and
electrons, and the arrangements of atoms in crystals or
large molecules. The classic example is the continuous
development of improved plastics and synthetic fibres that
has stemmed from the discovery that they are composed
of long, chain-like molecules. But in metals and ceramics,
too, exploration of the sources of strength and weakness,
of the effects of alloying, manufacturing techniques,
deformation in service and corrosion, is providing steady
improvement and economy in the use of these materials.
In particular, we know now that all normal materials
are far weaker than they might in principle be, because
of the presence of microscopic flaws or irregularities.

The tantalizing discovery of "whiskers", fine flawless
filaments of many different substances, shows that ideal
materials, ten or a hundred times stronger than those we
have now, are not ruled out. At present, whiskers are
expensive to make and tricky to use. But the same quest

for material perfection has led to the development of silica fibres of astonishing strength, and to glasses and ceramics far less brittle than those to which we are accustomed. In due course, these advances will bear fruit, and our structures and vehicles may acquire a gossamer lightness combined with great durability. Meanwhile, the available materials, as always in human history, set limits to what we can do; and materials scientists find urgent demands from their fellow engineers for stuff that will withstand great temperatures, or corrosive environments, or the radiation within a nuclear reactor or out in space.

For structural materials, scientists and engineers are beginning to look afresh at the biological world, and to marvel at the extraordinary structures evolved by nature, in the form of bone, hair, skin, wood, and so on. We have much to learn, but it is already clear, for example, that nature commonly makes use of composite materials, analogous to, but subtler than, glass-fibre reinforced plastics. There is no doubt that we shall imitate nature more closely in our materials. Already, for example, there are materials available that work on the same principle as muscle, contracting or relaxing when bathed in different solutions. Living tissue also teaches us how excellent are the materials to be made from substances as common as dirt, and encourages us to look afresh at what we can do with, say, sand or ice.

Organizational resemblance to living tissue is only part of the story. We shall find out how to make our structures self-repairing. And, taking the techniques of crystal-growing much further, we shall make some, at least, of the components of our structures take shape by growing rather than by moulding or working.

From another point of view, imitation of nature has

already reached the point where surgeons can replace very many of the parts of the living body, at least experimentally, with artificial materials or machines. We have come a long way from wooden legs and false teeth. Plastic lenses for the eye, artificial bone, artificial hearts and kidneys, very life-like artificial limbs controlled by nerve signals—these are already with us. In time, no doubt, we shall be able to replace virtually any organ, excepting the brain but including, in cases of paralysis, key sections of the nervous system. Even the general deterioration of old age may be in part at least amenable to treatment as a problem in materials science, if we can pin it down to an accumulation over the years of faulty molecules in the tissue, which may be eliminated by chemical means. At first the application of any such techniques of repair will properly be directed to improving health throughout the normal human life span. Eventually, we need not doubt, marked extension of the life span to, say, 200 years, will become possible and the tricky question will arise of how long people want to, or should, be kept alive.

Nor are we confined, in our repairs of the human body, to implanted organs made artificially. Beyond the present attempts to transplant living organs such as kidneys from one person to another, and the further possibility of transplanting organs from animals to men (both of which unfortunately depend on overcoming the natural mechanisms whereby the body rejects foreign tissue) other hopes arise. We know that the development of the human body from a formless egg involves "differentiation", wherein cells acquire different characteristics according to the tissues and organs—nerve, bone, blood, and so on—for which they are intended. But it seems that most cells retain the full genetic material characteristic of the body as a whole, with their relevant parts suppressed. Thus the genetic material in each cell could potentially give rise to any other kind of tissue, if only we knew how to switch the appropriate genes on and off. Current fundamental research is beginning to disclose partial answers. When we have discovered more about it, it may become feasible to grow replacements for worn-out organs within the body itself, from its own tissues. A strange by-product of this train of thought is the idea of "clonal reproduction", in which the set of genes taken from an individual can be cultured in such a way as to produce an infant which is technically his identical twin—what Joshua Lederberg has called "the narcissistic perpetuation of a given genotype".

Other properties of materials are now at least as significant as their structural applications. Here, too, the modern atomic viewpoint gives us a sound basis for industrial development.

One group of materials of exceptional interest at the present time and into the foreseeable future are the super-conductors. For many years these were in the nature of laboratory curiosities—astonishing in their ability to conduct electric currents with absolutely no resistance but seemingly without application. The situation has been changed radically by the discovery of the so-called "hard" superconductors, alloys which retain their superconduc-tivity even when they are called upon to do serious "work", which for practical purposes means sustaining a high magnetic field. Superconductivity is somewhat cumbersome to achieve, because the materials have to be cooled to extremely low temperatures before they lose their electrical resistance, but the practical benefits in the form of very powerful magnets for compact electrical machinery are such that it will be well worth the trouble.

Meanwhile there are somewhat vague hopes that materials will be found which remain superconducting up to much higher temperatures. There is a range of other curious phenomena at very low temperatures, still imperfectly understood, which one day, no doubt, will find practical uses: one well-known example is superfluidity, in which a liquid simply climbs out of any open vessel in which it is put.

Interest also centres on semiconductors—those materials which are neither excellent conductors of electricity like copper nor good insulators like glass but are susceptible to control of their conductivity in all manner of subtle ways. Hence the transistor and hence, too, the "microminiaturization" of electronic circuits to the point where the guts of a powerful computer can be carried in the pocket. When these are combined with new magnetic materials used for storing information, and ways of etching components so small as to be invisible in an ordinary microscope, there is no end to the reduction in scale of our electronic devices until we reach the physical limits of atoms and molecules. We should certainly be able to fit a machine as complex as the human brain into a volume no greater than the human skull.

It is not yet at all clear in detail how the brain works, but both learning and thought may well turn out to involve the chemical establishment of pathways and barriers to nervous impulses. Whatever the answer (and it cannot be long delayed) we shall again be able to imitate nature in our computing machines—and, whether or not the details of mechanism are closely similar, the next great step which turns the computer from merely an advanced calculator into a learning and thinking machine will surely follow.

Moreover, twin possibilities may follow for enlarging the capacity of the human brain. There is reason to suspect that our brains work very "inefficiently" and that, by manipulation by drugs or otherwise, we might be able to turn ourselves into super-geniuses. Closely related is the possibility of connecting the human brain directly to a computer. At its simplest, this would merely be a rationalization of the "man-machine interface", but it might be extended to such a bizarre possibility as "decanting" a human mind into a machine. I hope we should be wise enough to resist this Faustus-like temptation, because it seems to me that it is the present balance between mind and body that keeps us sane and what we choose to call human.

Short of permanent interference with the normal human brain (which could be an insidious process developing from the present-day use of tranquillizers and pep pills), a better knowledge of how the brain works will be of immense benefit in treating the mentally ill. Indeed, we can expect to see as great an assault on mental disease as there has been against bodily—and especially infectious— disease in the past few decades. Just as medical advances have shown us that prevention is better than cure, and that good physical health requires a disease-free environment, good food and exercise, so progress in mental health will involve a much more practical understanding of what we mean by "happiness" and the environmental conditions needed to secure it. We do not regard as healthy a man who suppresses disorders with endless pills; no more will we admire the man who keeps his mental balance and alertness only through drugs. There is, of course, great scope for the development of materials like Aldous Huxley's *soma*, and perhaps we shall find wise uses for hallucinogenic drugs; certainly safer substitutes for tobacco and alcohol are greatly to be desired. Unlike some pessimistic commentators, I do not believe that men are likely to spend their lives in a drugged state, unless the environment they create remains unbearable for many.

TOWARDS SATIATION

Machines are already becoming more "life-like" in their ability, through a wide range of automatic control techniques, to carry out elaborate operations themselves and to maintain a sort of inner balance comparable with the regulation of temperature and blood pressure in the human body. Even existing computers give a quite convincing impression of intelligence, at least to those who have not written the programmes and don't know how the tricks are done. Automation is extending itself slowly but inexorably into almost every branch of industry, and probably eventually into almost every human activity.

This is not the place for a detailed discussion of the techniques of automation. By way of illustration, let it suffice to say that, at present, control of a chemical manufacturing plant or accounting in a bank are relatively easy to automate; complex assembly of manufactured goods along conventional lines is more difficult, but that only suggests that designers have not yet adapted themselves to the needs and opportunities of automation. As design itself becomes automated, and drawings are converted directly into instructions for fabricating and assembly tools, this problem will tend to take care of itself. Manufacture of computers, in particular, is potentially very well suited to automation, so that the "self-reproduction" of automatic machinery becomes very plausible. It then requires only the automation of mining and materials-preparation to make the "mass production of the means of mass production" quite an easy process.

Lest monstrous pictures be conjured up by this phrase, let me hasten to say it is a fallacy that automation can be applied profitably only in mass-production of identical articles. That view arises from the fact that automatic machinery tends to be expensive and, in conventional production-engineering terms, that means long runs to spread the cost. In certain forms of automation, particularly in the transfer lines where parts travel from one tool to the next for precise treatment of a hard and fast kind, that is indeed the case. What matters (by present economic standards) is that the machinery should be kept fully occupied. If, as can perfectly well be the case, the automatic machines are flexible, and able to carry out programmes in response to computed instructions which can be changed from one job to the next, variety is created at will. The computer, too, can help with the preparation of varied designs and with the stock-keeping involved in handling non-standard parts.

What is also not understood by many people, outside and even inside industry, is that the saving in labour is usually a secondary consideration in automation. The immediate practical aim has more to do with increasing efficiency in other respects: faster throughput, economy of materials, tighter control of quality, full control of operations inherently so rapid that the human brain and hand are not really quick enough to cope. What is true of the control of a high-speed aircraft is also true of the operation of a steel mill or a bank: machines are often smarter

than men, at least in the narrow compass of their special-
ities. Nevertheless, the redundancies will occur. And
young men today embarking on careers which they may
be expecting to pursue to the end of a normal working
life—that is to say, well into the twenty-first century—
would be well advised to take account of technical and
other changes that may radically alter the present
assumptions about "prospects". Even the most venerable
professions, such as law and medicine, will not be un-
affected.

There are conflicting views about how quickly or otherwise automation is going to multiply productivity and
reduce the requirements for human labour. The limits
are at first set, in my opinion, simply by human enterprise
and by the initial supply of capital; successful automation
will thereafter generate such surpluses for reinvestment
that the process will snowball. We are more likely to
underestimate rather than overestimate the speed of
advance, at least in the richer countries.

Beyond that, there are other limits in the availability of
raw materials for manufacture. From one point of view,
those limitations are severe and the outlook is bleak. Man
kills, mines, burns, consumes, and wastes the elements and
their precious combinations; the alchemy of sunlight, soil,
and rocks is hard put to it to make good the losses. In some
cases replenishment is impossible in principle: when man
makes an animal species extinct it stays extinct. In other
cases, the time-scale is all wrong: nature is still perfectly
capable of making fresh coal, oil, metalliferous ores and
soil, but the rate at which man is burning the fossil fuels,
mining the ores, and eroding the soils outpaces their
natural replacement. The continuing discoveries of new
mineral deposits, and the belief that under the jungles of

Brazil or the waters of the continental shelf lies the new El Dorado, give us short-term confidence. But we know there must be limits, and with such large populations to maintain and with their desires for material affluence, any serious discussion of man's future must include a resources budget; in particular, as a matter of economic and political prudence, it must allow qualitative judgements about the uses to which the readily available resources should be put.

Yet, from a different point of view, the limits on raw materials are much less severe. Every element man needs is present in considerable quantities on and in the Earth; every compound that he needs can be synthesized. It is only a matter of energy supplies and of the lengths to which men are prepared to go to obtain raw materials when the richest ores are exhausted. For example, there is plenty of aluminium in clay; but at present, while there is still bauxite to be had, it is scarcely economic to try to extract it. If we are forced to turn to lower-grade ores, there will be scope for developing new extraction methods and, in this connection, it is significant that microbes and plants often show an ability to concentrate traces of certain elements present in their environment.

In principle, too, there is an almost unlimited supply of minerals dissolved in the waters of the oceans; here again, however, we have to assume either generous supplies of energy or subtle biological processes if we are to recover them. Nor should we forget the great mass of the Earth under our feet. The crust where geological and biological action has concentrated elements in readily accessible forms is really quite thin. Beneath it lies a huge quantity of assorted elements; but even if we could get at them they will almost certainly take the form of a uniform composition of dull stone. Only if men one day find a means of inducing, on a large scale, those natural metamorphoses that have created the rich ores of the crust is any really deep quarrying likely to be contemplated.

It is my belief that before men reach the limits to automated production set by the availability of materials, they will be satiated with their material wealth. If human greed is kept within bounds, and if attention is paid to durability of products and recovery of scrap, the net requirements of materials can be quite modest. But this conclusion depends upon a change in economic systems, such that continuing prosperity does not rely on ever-increasing consumption of the products of automatic factories, and also upon the assumption that there will be plenty of energy.

THE SOURCES OF POWER

All the energy of the universe, excepting only that released on a cosmic scale by gravitational collapse of stars or by other effects of gravitational origin like the tides, comes from transformations of atomic nuclei. Even the traditional source of energy, firewood, derives from the Sun's nuclear furnace via sunlight and photosynthesis. Coal, and probably oil and natural gas as well, also derive from solar energy, although they store the sunlight of millions of years ago. The rate of replenishment of coal and oil is so low that the best fields will be worked out in the foreseeable future; we know that the discovery of oil reserves continues and that there may be rich new fields under the continental shelf, but we also know that they seem in principle to be limited.

Another manifestation of the Sun's energy converted to useful form is the harnessing of falling water, which was in the first place raised by evaporation from the oceans; similarly the energy that drives a windmill arises from the unequal heating of different parts of the Earth's surface.

Attempts to harness the Sun's energy directly have not, so far, been a notable success except in the very special case of Earth satellites and space probes, many of which rely on their panels of solar cells to keep their batteries charged. These solar cells are the fruit of modern knowledge of semiconducting material, but they remain rather expensive and their applications on Earth are confined to such purposes as the powering of rural telephone exchanges and of navigational buoys. But, as engineers become more expert in these conversion processes, we can expect solar power to come into its own as a major source of energy, unless or until we can set up our own "suns" on Earth, in the form of nuclear fusion plant.

The release of nuclear energy has seemed fateful for our generation, but economically it has been a stroke of good fortune. Without it, the prospect of conventional fossil fuels becoming exhausted would be terrifying. There are two approaches to the release of nuclear energy on Earth, both pioneered by the bomb-makers. Both depend on the conversion of mass to energy. The nuclei of the atoms of all the great range of elements created by cosmic transformations are composed of whole numbers of particles (protons and neutrons), but it so happens that elements in the middle of the range are slightly lighter than one would expect from a simple aggregation of these particles. Accordingly, if the lightest elements are "fused" or the heaviest elements are "fissioned", to produce other elements in or nearer to the middle range, some mass disappears and energy appears in its place. In the A-bomb, and in existing nuclear power stations, it is the latter, fission process which is applied to the heavy metals uranium and plutonium; in the H-bomb, as in the Sun, fusion is used to build hydrogen into helium, but, while the Sun works with ordinary hydrogen, man-made fusion requires heavy forms of hydrogen.

Fission power stations have recently become competitive, in certain situations, with power stations using fossil fuels. The Earth's stock of uranium and, using a more elaborate process, thorium, thereby become extremely important additions to the world's fuel reserves. During the next few decades, fission power will tide us over and meet many of the additional demands for energy. But the supplies of rich uranium and thorium ores are not unlimited and, while it may one day be economic to extract the traces of these metals from ordinary rock, that would be a cumbersome business. Another drawback of the fission power programmes is that the reactors create huge quantities of radioactive waste material, which has to be buried with great attention to safety.

For these reasons, there is every incentive to adapt the H-bomb fusion process to peaceful purposes, by trying to create (in magnetic bottles, because no material walls will do) extremely high temperatures such as those existing in the interior of the Sun. The practical difficulties are very great but, in spite of some Jeremiahs among the theoreticians, there is no real reason to doubt that success will ultimately crown the efforts of physicists in many countries to tame the wriggling "plasmas" of hot gas, or that we shall see at least prototype fusion stations in operation in this century. As a last resort, if present approaches should indeed prove to be hopeless, we might in principle be able to use H-bombs themselves, exploded underground, storing, in a great mass of material, heat to be tapped at will. If it came to that, however, I believe that renewed attention towards exploiting sunlight would be a wiser policy.

Given fusion power, the consequences will be profound. The fuel will be the heavy hydrogen present in small amounts in all the water of the oceans and rivers, representing reserves of energy beyond our previous dreams. Energy supplies will no longer be a limitation to human ambitions or wealth. Fusion will be the counterpart to automation in accomplishing the final solution to the "economic problem". What is politically of immense significance is that the successful accomplishment of this programme will end for ever the privileges of energy, such as those which have given great benefit to the owners of coal and oil deposits and are now coming to favour people with uranium ores. Everyone will have effectively equal access to energy. (Much the same, it should be noted, applies to solar energy, if that should be developed instead, except that here the tropical regions have an advantage.) Moreover, self-sufficiency in energy will encourage self-sufficiency in other respects, particularly in the use of raw materials which can be extracted from low-grade ores or sea-water, if there is sufficient energy to hand. In short, our ideas about trade, economics, and the strategy of wealth, will undergo a revolution.

Before leaving nuclear energy, it is just worth mentioning that a remarkable fraction of the energy released by nuclear reactions from the Sun and other stars takes the form of neutrinos. These are energetic but very elusive atomic particles that possess neither charge nor mass; they can pass through the Earth and out the other side as easily as a bullet through fog. It may be that we inhabit an ocean of neutrinos, filling space as gas molecules fill a room. It is a remote, but not altogether inconceivable possibility that, in their researches into the nature and behaviour of neutrinos, physicists may find some way of trapping this neutrino energy.

Two other sources of energy are worth mentioning, because they are of current interest, although only in limited areas. One is the tides. In certain narrow straits and bays where the tides are, as it were, focused by local geography, the waters heaved by the Sun and the Moon as the Earth rotates attain interesting heights of rise and fall: the Gulf of St Malo, the Bay of Fundy, and the narrows near Archangel are perhaps the best examples. Yet, contrary to the impression given by the heavings of billions of tons of water, there is not a vast source of energy here: the very construction of barriers and turbines to harness the tides tends to damp them out and so, great though the individual works may one day be, their contribution to world energy supplies will be small.

Natural radioactivity and movements within the Earth's crust afford a tremendous supply of heat under our feet. This infernal heat manifests itself in volcanos and in geysers and volcanic springs. In New Zealand, Italy, Iceland, the United States, the Soviet Union, and elsewhere, serious efforts have been made to harness it. Its use is likely to be confined to those areas where it is brought to the surface by natural means. Wherever one sinks a shaft, it is true, the temperature rises as one goes downwards and there has been talk of running water pipes to collect this heat and bring it to the surface. The chief snag, however, is the poor heat conduction of the rocks; the surroundings of a pipe would be quickly cooled and one would have to wait some time for them to warm up again. Similar objections may apply to the "last-resort" idea of exploding H-bombs underground as a source of heat.

LINKS AND PASTIMES

Other great themes of current applied science, ranking with developments in materials, machinery, power supplies, and so on, are perhaps more familiar to the man in the street: communications and transport. But in the former case, while developments such as television and communications satellites are well appreciated, there may be too little sense of the vast growth in the transfer of information we can expect. Already in the United States there are television-telephones; already business of many kinds is conducted by networks of computers and computers linked by communications lines which are themselves computer-controlled; already there is a general increase in the electronic facilities in each living-room. These trends will reach to the point where high-capacity communications cables are installed in each home, like the water or electricity supply.

There may also be a negative connection between communications and travel. Talking to people face to face by private television, and the rapid exchanges of information of all kinds via computers, can make it unnecessary for a man to leave his office, perhaps even his home, to do his business. For those who do want to travel, the automobile will pass its peak of esteem and we shall see a revival of high-speed railway-like public transport (this process is beginning in the USA). Air travel and air transport of freight will continue to grow prodigiously, and after the supersonic aircraft, with its troublesome "boom", we shall have the even faster "hypersonic" passenger aircraft flying much higher and faster still. The hovercraft and other air-cushion vehicles will gain wider acceptance, particularly in the under-developed countries where they reduce the need for proper roads; but noise tells against them, too, and I believe that noise, or lack of it, will be the ultimate criterion of choice between rival transport systems. For this reason, interest in airships will revive.

The number of men and women who will travel into space during the next century may be numbered only in hundreds, and yet the human stage will in a real enough sense be extended by their voyages and those of un-manned spacecraft to encompass much of the solar system. If for most of the people on Earth the space adventure will be a vicarious one, the participation in development and production of space vehicles will be on a very large scale. We can expect to see scientific stations set up on the Moon and Mars, although colonization in the manner envisaged by many science-fiction writers appears to be very remote; remote, too, seems the possibility of bringing anything useful back to Earth from those bodies unless it happens to be a plant of economic value, analogous to the discovery of tobacco and potatoes by the early navigators. For practical benefits we have to look nearer home to satellites operating in sublunary space in aid of weather forecasting, navigation, and communications. Activities in deep space are best regarded as an interesting pastime for the human species.

Terrestrial science, too, will form a major activity for mankind, pursued as much out of interest as for any practical pay-off. From being a somewhat eccentric occupation it will become a sizeable "industry", occupying 10 per cent or more of all human effort. Much of it will consist of small-scale experiments and observations, but there will also be "big science" projects—particle accelerators, oceanic stations, giant telescopes, large-scale biological studies, and the like, ranking with space probes as major undertakings involving not only big teams of scientists and engineers but also massive constructional and servicing operations. And if the public grudges non-productive science so large a chunk of the available resources, scientists will be entitled to point out that the wealth of nations has grown on the discoveries of science more than on any other activity.

ARE WE TO BE TRUSTED?

We have rambled pretty freely through the technical world of today and tomorrow, without regard for the conventional mental boxes of the specialists; but I have deliberately left aside until now a discussion of the military prospects. Armouries can draw on almost the whole repertoire of technologies, and to consider future weapons provides a kind of black recapitulation of the possibilities —including even some of those in Chapter 3, concerned with increasing world food production. This exercise of "You name it—I can use it" in the military field is the most appalling commentary on present human attitudes to the powers arising from natural knowledge.

"You name it"—why not start with the efforts to control the diseases of plants and animals, which rob the hungry of their food? The isolation of the causative agents—pathogens—for study and for the preparation of vaccine, provides ready-made economic weapons which, distributed by agents among the crops and herds of an opponent, could play havoc with his agricultural economy. Such measures could be employed in nominally peaceful circumstances to bring a rival to his knees; conversely, natural outbreaks of agricultural disease may be attributed, in times of tension, to enemy agents, and foot-and-mouth disease could cause a war.

As everyone knows, pathogens of human diseases, too, are being cultivated as possible weapons and their potency will tend to increase as natural disease is eradicated and the acquired resistance of populations diminishes. We need not doubt, either, that an early application of genetic manipulations of organisms may be directed to the creation of novel diseases against which no immunity exists and no vaccines can be stockpiled.

Closely allied in military thinking to these biological weapons is the development of chemical-warfare agents. These range from defoliating materials, for denying natural cover to an enemy, to drugs for attacking the nervous system for purposes of temporary incapacitation or destruction of the will to resist. The latter type of drug in turn links up with techniques of psychological warfare using threats, cajolery, and more subtle mind-bending techniques, via modern channels of communication. If present experiments on the remote control of animals with electrical brain implants are taken at their face value, it is a short step to envisaging humans enslaved by similar means; indeed, we might by our own folly invite such an outcome, if brain implants should become fashionable as a means of titillating our emotional centres as television titillates our eyes and ears.

But the military man scarcely needs human robots to

fight his larger wars, given the great repertoire of electronic devices now dedicated to military purposes. Just as the development of computers was encouraged by military needs (for the design of nuclear weapons, the co-ordination of air defences, and the control of individual weapons systems) so the "super-computer", or learning machine, is finding its first uses in weapons, and we can expect to see the development of electronic Napoleons which will suggest (or order?) strategical moves. At a lower level, computers and learning machines can be used for all kinds of purposes in the field, including staff work, while micro-miniaturized devices make possible the incorporation of evasion and tracking systems of great sophistication in individual missiles.

Here the existing types of nuclear weapons enter the discussion, as warheads on missiles and anti-missile missiles and counter-anti-missile-missile missiles, in a prospective arms race of fantastic cost as each participant tries to maintain his own "deterrent" and to reduce by a few millions the number of lives he may lose to an attacker. It is the expense and desperate character of such technological rivalry that could make the Doomsday Machine, so far a hypothetical device for destroying all life on Earth, appear to some military planners a preferable alternative, as the ultimate "deterrent". Such a weapon is certainly conceivable; it could, for the sake of illustration, take the form of a huge nuclear bomb (or a number of bombs) designed to distribute lethal levels of radioactivity over the whole surface of the planet.

Short of Doomsday, there may be other ways of producing major distortions in the Earth's environment along the lines of climate control. Among the broad possibilities of tampering with the ice, ocean currents, and air passages mentioned in Chapter 3, men may try to give new literal meanings to "cold war" and "hot war", in worsening the climate of an opponent. And in the upper atmosphere it may become possible to destroy for a while, over a selected target area, the thin layer of ozone which has protected vegetation and animals from the deadly "sunburn" of ultraviolet radiation since the time when living things first ventured ashore from the oceans.

Beyond the atmosphere, spacecraft are being employed for continuous surveillance of opponents' territory, and the Americans have already deployed a small anti-satellite system in case satellites should acquire more sinister purposes. Although there are serious doubts about whether there is any military sense in the stationing of nuclear and other weapons in near-Earth orbit or farther away in space, it is quite credible that for psychological reasons the powerful nations will come into open conflict for "mastery of space".

Possible operational significance in the penetration of men and submersibles to the greatest ocean depths, the existence of missile-carrying submarines, and the continuing strategic importance of shipping combine to put a definite military bias on the present interest in the oceans. Thus the rediscovery of the oceans, potentially so valuable to man as an immense farm or playground, is giving us new battlegrounds, wherein hunter/killer submarines will stalk their prey amid a network of nuclear mines and detection fences.

In this consideration of weapons technology, as in the review of apparently constructive opportunities, I have not tried to be exhaustive. For example, I have said nothing explicit about the laser, that new source of light of unprecedented purity, which can be used for welding metal, analysing information, communicating across space—or blinding the enemy's infantry. Nor have I dwelt on biological experiments that could make human reproduction a matter of babies in bottles, as Aldous Huxley foresaw, because I suspect most people find the natural arrangements quite satisfactory.

Throughout, I have tried to show the range of present knowledge and the interconnections between understanding, technique, and human consequences. I have deliberately chosen to emphasize bizarre possibilities and the reason may now be plain. We have fantastic powers already—in nuclear energy, in rockets, in drugs, in television, and so on—but we have grown so accustomed to them that we do not often stop to ask what serious human purpose they are to serve. The all-embracing facility of our present-day military and economic machinery adopts them, puts price tags on them, and thereby pretends to have evaluated them.

By looking ahead to other possibilities—full automation, learning machines, controlled nuclear fusion and so on—to which we are not yet accustomed, we may be induced to question more urgently the ends of all these means, the existing as well as the foreseen. In that case, I believe we may be led to consider afresh the accepted aims and conduct of our civilization. And just as reflection on the human species' Palaeolithic origins raises doubts about whether our agricultural habits are well matched to human nature, so consideration of our growing ability to modify human nature, by biochemical and biological means, must make us wonder whether we can continue to entrust the uses of such means to a social system whose criteria are those of money and power.

CHAPTER 5

A New Twist to the Plot

To the foregoing technical opportunities must now be added another which, in the long run, will surpass them all. A future historian may well remark that we are as blind to its implications as our predecessors were to science. Like the invention of modern science itself in the seventeenth century, it concerns an abstract notion. Just as that event triggered a vast growth in real knowledge about physical forces and the nature of inanimate materials and living organisms, so the new thing will open up areas that have hitherto been accessible only to methods of research less powerful than science, relying on authority, opinion, dialectic, piecemeal fact-gathering—in short, on books rather than on observation of nature. The innovation is a set of techniques, not yet codified like experimental science, for dealing rationally and comprehensively with *complex* systems.

Science is, in aggregate, very complicated, but in practice for the working scientist it is, almost by definition, simple to the point of naïvety. To answer a straightforward question may entail complex apparatus and months or years of experiment—but straightforward the questions must be, according to the traditions of modern science, and by the nature of the experimental method that has so far amply met the requirements of technical progress.

Hypotheses must not be multiplied; element by element the scientist seeks to build a tower of knowledge which, though parts may from time to time need renovation, will stand as a whole unshakeably for centuries if not for ever.

To do so, the experimenter has sought to control the wayward, or as he would call it, "trivial", variations in reality that might confuse his search for underlying principles. The modern scientist is happier in analysis than in synthesis: in breaking down the natural world into its components and describing each in isolation, rather than in attempting to comprehend the interaction of those elements in the world we observe daily with our own eyes.

Pendulums are good controllers of clocks, but the scientist prefers to replace them, in his thinking, by a point mass hung on a weightless string and swinging in a vacuum—and even then not boldly, like a real pendulum, but barely perceptibly, so that the mathematics become more tractable and the true beauty of natural law becomes apparent. But such procedures are of little help where the complexity of the real world really matters—most notably in human affairs.

A number of contemporary developments in science, technology, and human affairs are forcing us to grasp the nettle of complex systems and to attempt to define the hitherto undefinable; and by what is not entirely a coincidence the means are to hand.

In the development of a system such as an electricity grid, a stage is reached when it is no longer sufficient to regard it as the sum of its parts (generators, transmission lines, local loads); one has to consider the properties of the system as a whole. Dissecting it for analytical purposes is self-defeating. Much the same is true of telephone networks, of the engineering of a computer, of the higher processes of the human brain, or of the interactions of plants, animals, and the physical environment in a biological community.

The experimental surgeon can sever a nerve connection in an animal to demonstrate by deletion its sensory or motor function; but to attempt the same approach in the cerebral cortex of man would not work, because thought seems to involve large areas of the brain working in (so far mysterious) harmony. The field biologist who wonders why a population of rabbits is suddenly multiplying, cannot confine his attention to the breeding habits of the rabbits; the reason may be one of a score of possibilities arising out of changes in the rabbits' environment.

One of the first of possible applications of computers to be suggested was automatic language translation. What could be simpler, it was thought, than to equip a computer with a built-in dictionary and a set of grammatical rules? Then one could feed in *Pravda*, or all the journals of the Soviet Academy of Sciences, and receive a translation far faster than even a team of human translators could serve it up. In spite of a great many man-years and computer-hours of effort, this goal is still far off. The computers can indeed produce very rapid transliterations from one language into another, but they are full of ambiguities and misconstructions. Now the machine-translation experts are being forced to realize that a language is a very complex system and translation depends on the communication of the author's *thought* to the translator, and its re-presentation in the second language. As machines do not yet think like people, only something analogous such as the employment of a new intermediate language, in which the sense can be faithfully recorded, seems likely to provide a technical solution. Even to accomplish that, however, requires something close to an analysis of human thought processes.

National economic planning, which is becoming an accepted responsibility of all governments, non-communist as well as communist, is also showing the need to describe complex systems. While it is a relatively straightforward matter to compute the coal requirements to meet a given steel order, the mind boggles at the thought of tracing links between steel production, education, and the price of coffee. All these things are indeed linked, however loosely, and to start with one cannot fix a target for steel unless one knows roughly where all the steel is to go. The whole study is further complicated because there are questions of timing ("When must the new steelworks be operational if we are to hit the target for motor-vehicle production?") and because one's national system is coupled to a global system. At any time technical progress at home and abroad can alter the assumptions about competitiveness, cost, and manpower.

Such, then, are some of the immediate requirements for a new approach to complex systems. But there are others, so far scarcely identified. Any reading of history shows that, in order to tell a coherent story within a reasonable compass, the historian is obliged to trace bold patterns of cause and effect that seem plausible to him, and almost inevitably fails to do justice to the complexity of event and of influences that we plainly see around us as history is made today. Thus it comes about that radically different interpretations can coexist even for something as recent and well documented as the origin of the Second World War. Now, it seems to me, the "truth" about that is a matter of immense importance if we are to avoid a Third World War. It is at least as significant, surely, as the development of a reliable second-strike missile system. But, while millions of dollars, pounds, or roubles and much highly-educated manpower can be urgently deployed to develop a missile, nobody in authority seems bothered at all about our profound ignorance or uncertainty about historical factors. But "truthful" history can only be attempted by seeing the world of the past as a continuous complex system, rather than as a collection of selected events.

Another example of present impotence is the failure of the world's bankers to devise a system of international finance, whereby a rich nation can transfer some of its surplus wealth to a poor nation without jeopardizing the standing of its own currency in the international exchange. Our ideas about money have not kept abreast of human needs; more particularly, money is a simplifying symbol, which now oversimplifies the increasingly complex relationships of material wealth. Until the complexity can be comprehended, and new ways of securing trust in financial matters can be devised, the bankers will stick doggedly to their gold.

One could multiply the examples, through the social sciences, art (or at least, aesthetics), and humanities. But perhaps enough has been said to indicate some areas in which extraordinary benefits could accrue if the processes of induction and logical analysis could be extended from simple natural systems to complex natural and artificial ones.

Reasons for thinking that we may indeed be on the brink of major developments of this kind are diverse. First in immediate importance is the existence of the computer. Its capacity for handling information opens a great door to solutions of some of these complex problems by "brute force" methods. Nowadays computers solve, as a matter of routine, simultaneous equations involving several hundred unknown quantities—for example, in the overall day-to-day conduct of an oil company's operations, deciding more precisely than men could do where the tankers should go, and what the wells and refineries should be producing. But the computer can also be used in a more exploratory way, to test very rapidly for relationships between different things or to calculate the consequences of a possible course of action. We may be sure that computers will soon be used empirically for searching, defining, or analysing very many complex systems—from law to fuel supplies—even before a new theory of complex systems is much developed.

One source for that theory, or perhaps one should say the language, for dealing with complex systems, already suggests itself: the idea of multi-valued logic, which has been regarded as a mathematical or philosophical curiosity for some time. It is associated particularly with the names of A. N. Whitehead and Bertrand Russell. Modern science has, since its inception, rested on the simplest and most familiar kind of logic, which distinguishes between "true" and "false" (the fact that inductive reasoning can never prove anything "true" in a strict sense is beside the point). In human affairs, and in many complex systems, things are not so simple. "Partly true" is a perfectly valid description of many statements about human affairs as this example shows:

The Pope is a man	(true)
The Pope is a woman	(false)
The Pope is a democrat	(only partly true, because he sometimes acts like an autocrat)

The Pope is a Man of God (only partly true, because
                          many people do not believe
                          in God)

True/false is a two-way switch in thinking. It is verbally
or mathematically quite possible to work with three-,
four- or ten-way switches.

Even in physics—the most naïvely "logical" of sciences—
it may be necessary to accept that simple two-valued logic
(known mathematically as Boolean algebra) is no longer
adequate for all its problems. Writing on this general theme
of complex systems in modern science, Dr M. S. Goodall
(*New Scientist*, vol. 20, p. 255) has observed:

> On this situation, quantum theory, even in its existing
> form, throws quite a remarkable light. For, although
> the final statements it makes concerning the results of
> sub-atomic experiments are two-valued ("true" or
> "false", Boolean) in character, the route by which they
> are obtained clearly involves something more. The
> particles are treated as waves, and the probability of
> finding them at particular places depends on the
> reinforcement or cancellation of mutually interfering
> trains of waves. In other words, the relative phase of
> a wave enters into, complicates and enriches the under-
> lying logic of quantum mechanics. The phase drops
> out in the subsequent calculation of the probability
> of a given experimental result because it is assumed
> that it should do so—in other words it is assumed that
> there can be only one correct evaluation. While this
> assumption of a two-valued "true" or "false" logic
> had had great utility as an approximation in existing
> physics, the theory should allow incomplete deductions
> of a three-valued type ("true", "false" and "partly

true") to be made. They will, and this is essentially the point of "triality", be necessary if we are to succeed in reconciling quantum theory with cosmology, and making it self-consistent.

Dr Goodall also draws attention to the important experimental evidence that "the human mind in its everyday functioning is not restricted by assumptions that go with two-valued logic". In this connection another, more empirical, approach to a mastery of complex systems comes in the attempts, mentioned briefly in the preceding chapter, to develop machines more like the human brain than are the early generations of computers. Here, the stimulus is largely military: by their nature, military systems have to cope with the unexpected and it is very difficult to programme a conventional computer in anticipation of all the operational conditions that a satellite or a supersonic fighter is likely to encounter. In mimicking the human brain, the engineer builds into his electronic machine an important element of chance and an ability to learn by experience, with its responses evoking "reward" or "punishment" from the instructor. A certain unpredictability on the part of the machine in operation is more than offset by its quick response to the unexpected —which is also, after all, the reason why men are still used to supervise complicated automatic machinery.

But we cannot be satisfied with such an approach to the analysis and management of complex systems, however effective such learning machines may be in practice, because we may not know precisely how they achieve their results. Even if the learning machine were made so that we could "freeze" it and see precisely how it is functioning at a given moment, that would not show us by what stages it attained that state; so while it may perform well enough it cannot explain to us its analysis of the complex system—any more than a skilled pilot can explain precisely how he landed a big airliner safely in a storm. If the study of complex systems is to be a science rather than an art, we still need the means—the mathematical language—for discussing them objectively.

Another theoretical step in this direction has been taken by a distinguished American systems engineer, Lofti Zadeh. He has developed the notion of "fuzzy sets". Set theory is a powerful mathematical device for handling entities by assigning them to sets. The Pope is a member of the sets of men, of Italians, of churchmen; but not of the set of women. Is he a member of the set of democrats? The difficulty is that "democrats" is a concept that is very fuzzily defined. It is also defined differently in different countries, but even if one adheres to the Anglo-American meaning of the term, there is no mistaking that the edges of the set of democrats are decidedly vague. Is a member of the House of Lords a democrat? Is a powerful civil servant a democrat? Is someone who votes in free elections for the abolition of democracy a democrat?

Conventional set theory is too clumsy an instrument for dealing with fuzzy sets, because each entity has to be placed firmly in or out of a given set. In fuzzy-set theory one assigns to each entity a *degree* of membership. For example, one may say the Lord Chancellor is 75 per cent a democrat; an anti-democrat who votes in democratic elections may be 10 per cent a democrat. Often such assignments will be arbitrary and controversial, but any rational person must admit they give a truer picture than straight either/or choices.

Zadeh, as an engineer, was led into fuzzy sets by a

technical problem—how to make a machine that can read handwriting, taking account of the great variability of the representations of the letters, so that a poor calligrapher's *w* may be in the fuzzy region on the boundary of the set of *w*s, where it might also be an *m* or *ru*. But it seems probable to me that the non-technical applications of fuzzy sets will be of much greater consequence.

There are other indications that contemporary science is beginning to define previously vague notions in human affairs. One is information theory, again developed for primarily technical reasons, to determine the transmitter power, or frequency range, needed to send signals at a given rate along a telephone line or over a radio link subject to "interference". Pioneering studies by Claud Shannon in the United States led to the definition of the information content of a message in terms of its improbability. This is not a surprising idea; any journalist can rank the following statements according to their news value, which is basically their unexpectedness:

> The Pope is going to Peking
> The Pope is going to London
> The Pope is going to Milan
> The Pope is staying in Rome

But the important thing is that information theory can, in principle at least, assign numbers to the information content of such messages, thus taking a big bite out of the area of human affairs considered to be reserved for "hunch", "intuition" or "value judgements".

Theory is not the only route to the study of complex systems. In more pragmatic ways, scientists have, since the start of the Second World War, brought a great deal of rationality into military and industrial operations, under the heading of "operational research". What began as studies of the co-ordination of radar information and interceptor fighters has now grown to encompass a great deal of military planning and also the operations of big companies. There are many facets of this work, but one management technique worth mentioning is critical-path scheduling. This is a means of specifying all the operations and time required for those operations in the completion of a complex project, such as building a power-station. When all has been set down, in the form of a network, a computer can find which series of operations fixes the minimum time required for the whole undertaking—the so-called "critical path". Management effort can then be concentrated on ensuring that operations on the critical path are carried out as swiftly as possible. Such a study may reveal, for example, that any delay by a sub-contractor in supplying windows may hold up the completion of the whole power-station.

In other situations, there may be elements of great uncertainty. In developing a novel product, snags may be encountered. To assist in planning such work, it is possible to construct networks to show one's present guesses about the probability of success at each stage, and the alternative paths in the event of difficulty. Such critical-path techniques are quite straightforward in concept, but often elaborate in practice. They can describe in a reliable and analytical way the complexities of human operations, from bathing a baby to developing the economy of a nation.

Enough has perhaps been said to show that men are indeed beginning to get to grips with the untidiness of real life, which has hitherto been regarded as lying outside the scope of science. We may be confident that these examples are just rough beginnings, equivalent to the work of isolated experimenters in the preamble to natural science. But with all the advantages of a scientific climate, of more rapid acceptance of new ideas and, not least, of computers, the embryonic science of complex systems is developing much faster than natural science did three centuries ago.

A word of caution is necessary. The development of a language for describing complex systems will proceed extensively, just as conventional mathematics has advanced during three centuries of natural science. But mathematics tells us nothing definite about the natural world: it provides only a means of expressing the results of observations and suggesting deductions that might be tested. Before the establishment of modern science, mathematicians and others attempted to substitute deduction for observation, with the result—among others—that when Copernicus and Kepler launched the Earth into orbit round the Sun they were contending with a superstitious presumption of geometrical perfection in the universe, that was mathematically very appealing but was simply wrong. The same may be true of precipitate attempts by the United States government to use computers in military policy-making. Because of the potential power of theories of complex systems, and their close applicability to everyday life, we shall have to be exceedingly careful to stick to the facts and, where subjective or hypothetical elements come in, these must be designated as such and treated with the same disrespect that they are accorded in natural science. This honesty is especially necessary because direct experiments in the human field are more awkward to arrange than in studies of the natural world, and the "simulation" experiments using computers that will largely fill the gap will perforce contain built-in assumptions. But, given due care, the benefits will be immense.

An obvious field of application is in social studies. The crude, *ad hoc* survey methods of the present day can be replaced by continuous and comprehensive collections of data which could be explored and correlated in much more ambitious ways than at present. The connections between work and environment, between mental health and politics, between crime and sport, between economics and psychology, could all become manifest and these complex-systems analyses could be the social equivalents of the theoretical syntheses in physics. Every individual could be documented in the social analyses, not to regiment and reduce him to a numerical nonentity but quite the reverse—to give proper weight to each man's needs, opinions, and idiosyncrasies. Government could come to be seen as an experimental programme in the social sciences; even international affairs and strategy might be founded on studies of the interactions of nations and their policies, done by coupling together the economic and social models of the various countries. Human irrationality and emotion will make their appearance, in their proper contexts, in the form of psychological models.

The conduct of human affairs in the light of what Asa Briggs has called "unconditional surrender to facts" should certainly not limit imagination and initiative. Who would suggest that scientific study of the natural world has had such an effect? The testimony of three centuries' inventions is that on the basis of knowledge acquired in a spirit of great humility and objectivity, men of daring and vision have achieved a rate of innovation outstripping activities in the political and social worlds. Far from devaluing human activity in a mechanistic universe, science and technology have glorified it. Contrast the self-confidence of, say, the Wright brothers with the helplessness of the typical politician confronted with an economic or military crisis. Yet it is only the sequence in which techniques of discovery have emerged that makes aerodynamics seem "easier" than human exchanges.

An expected consequence of a flowering of the social sciences will therefore be a great inventiveness in public affairs. Such social innovations as there are nowadays—state medicine, life peerages, "teach-ins" and so on—are based on bright ideas or the logic of circumstances, rather than on a firm base of understanding. Racial integration, crime prevention, and world development are but three examples of areas in which constructive new thinking is desperately needed but is scarcely even attempted.

I cannot guess at the categorical solutions that complex-systems analysis may offer to, say, racial intolerance, any more than Francis Bacon, speculating about the natural sciences, could have written down Maxwell's equations of electromagnetism. But an analogy is suggestive. The view that one's own race or nation is significantly superior to another is like the ancient belief that men are a special creation divinely separate from other animals. Charles Darwin's evidence to the contrary did not immediately dispel the old ideal, because the mundane consequences were relatively unimportant. But, if the social sciences can establish, with great detail and authority, the qualities of all men and can make us more curious about those we regard as different, the old prejudices will crumble; and if they can also demonstrate with the necessary authority the practical advantages of integration, the whole rotten structure will be swept aside by self-interest.

Inseparable from this new complex-systems approach

to the social sciences will be the fresh start with history, hinted at earlier. It is no longer far-fetched to envisage the collection, weighting, and indexing of all historical records and archaeological evidence in a common system. Practically everyone who ever lived, at least in more recent times, would figure in such records, along with information about trade, climate, health, and all the other factors governing human life. Perhaps the system will even incorporate a rudimentary genetic analysis of inborn characters. At first, such a system will be constructed piecemeal by a new generation of historians applying data-processing methods to their particular fields of interest. But as the store of knowledge grows, selection of data will become less arbitrary and the need to rely on graphic "theories" to make order out of chaos will pass. The emergent story will be untidier, but for that very reason more faithful to human life.

If this programme is carried through successfully we may even reach a point at which we not only have the record tolerably straight but can carry out serious historical experiments of the "Cleopatra's nose" variety. Would the history of the world have been notably different if Cleopatra's face had been unattractive to the Romans? It is not just an academic pastime to ask questions like this. For practical purposes—including knowing what causes may be worth dying for—it would be highly desirable to assess what human actions and decisions have really mattered, and which were of little consequence because blind economic and social forces dominated the outcome. Operational researchers make a useful distinction between "decision-sensitive" and "decision-robust" situations in military and industrial matters, which serves to indicate where careful judgement is needed and where it is not. The new history may provide future decision-makers with just such a contrast of the human and systematic forces at work.

To achieve results of this kind, in history and in all other studies, the techniques of storing and retrieving information in an electronic form need urgent development. Anyone who has tried to cross-index or classify books knows that no simple system is satisfactory, because little that is interesting fits neatly into isolated compartments. Creative thought—another complex process we understand but meagrely—seems to operate by finding connections between apparently disparate things. How can a librarian, whether human or electronic, provide the research worker with the information and inspiration he needs, even in his present narrow-minded activities? How, in our broader programme, can a man get at the information he needs—neither too little nor too much?

Here again, the complex-systems approach will provide new answers, by permitting the design of information-retrieval systems more closely matched to the ways in which we think. If a user asks for information on a particular subject-combination—let us say, infectious disease in Ancient Rome—the machine will search the medical and historical literature looking for Rome in one and disease in the other. But it will also sample closely related literature concerning disease in the Roman Empire and sanitation, housing, and vermin in the city of Rome. If the latter arouses the user's interest he can pursue the resulting train of thought in any direction. The time will come when it will be hard to tell whether the research worker or the librarian is really responsible for the generation of new ideas.

If mechanical storage and retrieval of information is

likely to be a methodological base of future scholarship, its scientific and moral core will lie in human ecology, the study of man as a biological entity in an environment compounded of physical and biological elements, both natural and man-modified. Here is the neglected germ of the great reunification of knowledge and life which can now be foreseen. Properly interpreted, ecology is all-embracing, but as it is practised at present it is particularly concerned with the success and tribulations of interacting plant and animal populations; human ecology concerns the effect of the environment on man, and vice versa, at a biological level. Physical disease and food supplies are plainly ecological matters, and are so regarded today. History, architecture, mental health, transport, and so on are all potential inputs for a more complete ecological study.

But as a further example of the possibility of developing our understanding of complex systems, let us concentrate on the narrower view of ecology as an exercise in field biology. Even here it is broad enough, amounting to what has been called the ability to "read the landscape". It combines the patient knowledge of animal behaviour and movements, which must have been a matter of everyday concern to the Palaeolithic hunters, with the sophistication of modern geology, meteorology, plant physiology, and biochemistry. It recognizes that no plant or animal can survive by itself, but forms part of a system of elaborate mutual dependence ranging from micro-organisms to giant trees, the "biotic community"; together with the physical elements, they form an "ecosystem". Wild life achieves extraordinary stability, such that a biotic community can survive for thousands of years with little change, but let man so much as fell a few trees and the system can be seriously disturbed. In his practice of agriculture, man has destroyed the natural communities over much of the world, often bringing ruin on himself in the process. There are few reservoirs left where we can study the magnificent "climaxes" of pre-human evolution.

At present, realization of the vulnerability of biological communities under human control is inadequately matched by the practice of this relatively new science of ecology. The numbers engaged have been few, the principles have been slow to emerge. In the current International Biological Programme, a substantial effort is being made to gather comparative data on biological conditions in many parts of the world. But the scale and complexity of the problem would call for much more massive efforts for purely human ends, such as policy-making for food production, even if we were not also in imminent danger of extinguishing many of the habitats and species that make the planet agreeable to live on.

A major advance in ecology will require more detailed mapping of soil, climate, and land use than has yet been attempted in most parts of the world; it will need rapid, computerized means of identifying the myriad of plant and animal species that inhabit a specified area; elaborate and often repeated census of key species by biologists in the field; careful watch on animal breeding and the movements of tagged animals; observation of feeding habits, including the predations of one animal species on another. Each area is grossly or subtly different from all others, and its proper management, whether for human use or wildlife conservation, requires detailed local knowledge. In short, it is an immense programme, calling for the deployment of far more biologists than are at present available because, however much complex-systems analysis may help in interpreting the results, and in integrating them with other scientific, historical, or social data, the basic observations have to be made in the field. What the new habits of thought and the ancillary data-processing machinery can do is to make the effort supremely worth while, both practically and intellectually.

For clarity, I have reviewed these applications of complex-systems analysis under conventional headings like "social studies", "history", and "ecology". But to do so smudges the important feature: that all learning itself forms a single complex system, and is only a part of the more complex system we call life, which in turn is part of the natural system of the universe. Given the techniques of synthesis, the traditional divisions of scholarship and expertise will fade. Of even greater consequence for human welfare is that our convenient moral compartments will also disintegrate, so that it will no longer be acceptable that a man can spend six days a week, say, training as a soldier and the seventh affirming, with Moses and Jesus, that killing people is wrong.

We talk polemically about "one world", meaning only that men must perforce be united at the political level. Before very long the phrase could have a much grander meaning, in which every natural process and every human action, now and in the past and future, will be seen as part of a composite system. It will not be an arid, deterministic system, but a rich, colourful picture of the world we inhabit, in which everything is interesting and in some sense subject to the human mind and will. Then we too shall care when sparrows fall, and pretend to a little wisdom.

CHAPTER 6

In Place of Agriculture

AMID THE triumphs and opportunities for the human mind outlined in the preceding chapters, one great anachronism stands out. It is that nearly all the thinking and activity about the most important economic function of all, the provision of food, still centres on the idea that the right way to do it is to catch the energy of sunlight in the green leaves of traditional cultivated plants spread over millions of square miles of the Earth's surface. This is so despite the manifest failure of agriculture adequately to feed the poorer people of the planet; despite, too, the growing number of scientists who speculate about more rational methods, and the smaller number actually investigating them.

It is, I believe, only a matter of time before engineers build factories that can make most or all of the kinds of food we need. This section is concerned with technologies that are likely to be involved. The question is whether the authorities and food industries will continue to ignore the possibilities until famine has taught its fearful lesson, or whether they will sponsor on an adequate scale the wide range of research and development needed to turn the possibility of factory-made food into reality.

The idea that agriculture is a "natural" method of growing food is deeply fixed in our minds. If we are to wipe the slate clean and think without prejudices about other ideas for getting food, it is worth recalling how unnatural the usual methods are.

Even the simplest agriculture is a violation of nature. The peasant of Asia is as revolutionary in one basic respect as the most science-minded farmer of north-west Europe. To take a patch of fertile land and to work at it until only one kind of plant is growing on it that season involves studied destruction of the "weeds" and the "pests", which really means getting rid of the natural diversity that obtains in virgin land. By hard work, skill, and water the farmer may make the patch more fruitful than it was before. To stand at the hedge (another artifact) and see a field of golden grain may properly fill the on-looker with delight at the works of man, but to call it "natural" is blindness. The variety of grain is itself man-made, in the sense that, but for selection and breeding, that kind of grass would not exist. Let the farmer neglect his field for a season or two and we shall see what nature will do: a riot of "weeds" will take over, as nature impro-vises with what is to hand to exploit wasted sunlight and to diversify again.

The modern farmer and husbandman goes further, of course. The war on intruders is greatly aided by potent weed-killers and insecticides. Indeed, as noted in Chap-ter 3, the newest weed-killers are so effective that it becomes possible to keep down weeds without using a plough. Fertilizers serve to match the natural soil to the farmer's special requirement. Livestock is bred by arti-ficial insemination, fed on factory-blended foodstuff, kept in pens or batteries, milked or slaughtered by mass-production methods. Many operations on the farm have become mechanized and susceptible to automation; farm planning can now be aided by computer.

There is nothing wrong here unless, locally, the poisons kill more than they were meant to or the animals are treated with needless cruelty. "Factory farm" has been used as a pejorative term; one can think it apt without accepting the sinister overtone. On the contrary, modern techniques are praiseworthy efforts to make food production more efficient—and who dares deny the importance of that? All I wish to make clear is that, when we tuck into our food, we are deluding ourselves if we think that anything in it, apart from fish and game, is "natural" in any real sense. Again, it is quite understandable that some of us prefer eggs from "free-ranging hens", or hand-ground flour, but let us be clear that those who do are simply choosing a slightly lower level of artificiality.

What may be wrong with present arrangements is the diet. If someone proposed to make a universal synthetic food, to be the principal food for much of the world, comprising a lot of carbohydrate, a little plant protein, and one or two vitamins, there would be an outcry. Yet the same mixture, in rice, is tolerated in the same capacity. The diets of much of the world are, as we have seen in Chapter 1, shockingly inadequate and therefore, in a very real sense, unnatural. An Indonesian would lead a more natural life with a belly filled entirely with synthetic food, if it kept him healthy, than he does in a state of chronic malnutrition.

Possible new kinds of crops were instanced in Chapter 3, but these represent merely a continuation of agriculture by other means. One could envisage industrialized food production based on a harvesting of wild plants and leaves. A step in this direction is N. W. Pirie's machine for smashing protein out of leaves. Without going into this possibility in any detail, it is hard to imagine that, applied universally, it would be more efficient than agriculture. It remains a potentially useful supplement to agriculture or to other forms of food production.

We must turn now to methods of producing food that are the very antithesis of agriculture, in the sense that they do not require large tracts of land (or ocean). I do not know of any ready-made, established method that could be applied immediately to make the bulk of the world's food by non-agricultural methods; so my approach here is not prescriptive, but illustrative.

The object is to feed by suitable artificial means 9,000 million people, the likely world population by the middle of the twenty-first century. There is legitimate interest in less ambitious schemes for simply supplementing existing diets, produced agriculturally, by concentrating on the production of protein or amino acids by methods of high efficiency. Experiments by British Petroleum in France and elsewhere, in which yeast has been grown on petroleum, indicate that two tons of petroleum can produce one ton of pure protein. If we assume that we should supply 50 grams of protein a day to 9,000 million people by such means, the petroleum required would be 160 million tons per year, which is small compared with the present production of crude oil (exceeding 1,000 million tons per year). But it would still account for only a small part of the human food requirement. Even if comparable efficiency can be obtained for production of *all* food from petroleum, so that for the time being it would be quite possible to use this source, the limits which we know must exist to petroleum reserves should discourage us from basing a replacement of agriculture on it. Nevertheless, protein from petroleum will be important as one of the earlier forms of novel foods, paving the way for more general synthesis.

What is envisaged is a system whereby a wide variety of food is produced from cheap raw materials using the best available sources of energy. That is the crucial point if man is to escape from the fields, which are, in principle, simply large and unwieldy surfaces for the inefficient collection of sunlight. As we shall see, there may be good reasons for continuing to tap sunlight as the primary source of energy, but if so we should seek much more efficient ways of using it, so that the areas required for food production are greatly reduced.

The popular myth that the day will come when science will feed a man on a few little pills each day is without foundation. Energy has to be supplied to the human body in a mild chemical form, which immediately implies a volume at least approaching that of present-day diets. Indeed, the aim of industrialized food production should be something as substantial and palatable as present meals in the prosperous countries. No dogmatic exclusion of living systems is involved: where they can be adapted to factory conditions they may have important advantages over purely chemical methods. In the interests of making the food as similar as possible to what we know we like, a most important step should be kept in mind. It is that nourishing but unpalatable primary food produced by industrial techniques—like BP's yeast from petroleum— may be fed to animals, so that we can continue to eat our customary meat, eggs, milk, butter, and cheese— and so that people in under-developed countries can have adequate supplies of animal protein for the first time.

For that matter, there need be no vindictive zeal to eradicate agricultural or horticultural activities or to prove that technologists know best. Fruit, in particular, has special pleasures and values, so that the groves, orchards, and vineyards are less likely to be replaced than land dedicated to the production of rice or beef. For those who use the tests of the market place it will be eventually, I believe, a simple matter of economics—that much nourishing food will be produced more cheaply by industrial than by agricultural methods; anyone wishing to pay relatively more for farm produce will doubtless be able to do so. (At the outset, however, there will be quite a struggle to establish the new methods commercially.) For those who prefer to think in terms of human needs, it is a matter of so organizing food production that no one goes hungry; because agriculture is failing it must eventually be replaced, or at least massively reinforced, by new methods.

ENERGY AND RAW MATERIALS

Attention focuses on the key ingredients of the human diet at the stage of digestion. If we choose to elaborate the complex proteins of beef we should realize that it is not fundamentally necessary to do so. It is wasted effort in the sense that, in digesting beef, our own enzymes break it down into its constituent amino acids. Thus we should identify amino acids as a key ingredient, rather than protein. At the same time we must not ignore the aesthetic qualities of beef nor—what is medically more important—the question of disorders or atrophy of the human digestive machinery that might develop if it had no protein to practise on.

The requirements at the stage of digestion can be listed thus:

Amino acids (from protein)
Glycerol and fatty acids (from fats)
Sugars (from starch)
Vitamins
Mineral salts

There is also a need for roughage to maintain normal intestinal action, which in present-day diets is largely supplied in the form of cellulose. There may be unidentified constituents of ordinary food that are essential for normal life. If so, they are likely to be required in very small amounts only, like the known vitamins, and so can be conveniently included as possible eventual extensions to the list of vitamins.

In chemical terms, the requirements are modest. With the exception of some of the vitamins, the key materials are all quite uncomplicated substances. We might simplify still further by looking beyond the stage of digestion to the fate of some of the materials in the course of metabolism. In particular, the metabolism of carbohydrates and fats goes through cycles involving very common stuff like acetic acid. Nevertheless, there may be difficulties of assimilation and metabolic balance if we try to penetrate the system at the simplest levels. There is little such danger if we stick to the requirements listed.

Given a suitable attack on the problem there is little reason to doubt man's ability to produce these materials more efficiently than by agriculture. The attack would be a threefold one, involving plain chemistry for some purposes, imitations of living chemistry for others and, where both these fail, or are less efficient, resort can be had to complete organisms, whether microbes or animals. As we shall see shortly, there is plenty of choice of methods, but it is too early to say which will find favour for economic or aesthetic reasons. In my opinion, there are possibilities of sufficient promise to remove doubts about the ultimate technical feasibility of a sufficiency of them. They also indicate targets for research and development, to perfect techniques that are economical of plant, power, and materials and that can be combined to make a generous range of palatable and nourishing foods.

To anticipate possible objections here, let me say that I do not think it is "cheating" to base my argument on unproved methods. The basic facts are that living organisms make food materials with the utmost ease but inefficiently for human purposes; and that chemists and biologists are learning both how the organisms do it and also how to achieve the same ends by similar or different means. It is for the reader to judge whether he sees in the present state of knowledge, as I do, a basis for a programme of applied research that should certainly succeed.

There is one overriding consideration that must guide thinking about artificially produced food, and that is energy. It operates regardless of the detailed techniques envisaged. Although, as I have said, farms collect the diffuse energy of sunlight inefficiently, the area involved is so great that the total energy converted into food is likewise large. If we think of replacing sunlight by artificial energy sources we should be prepared for some startling statistics. The problem of "the energy barrier" is developed in detail in the Appendix; in summary it is as follows:

The energy contained in food is equivalent to a large fraction of the total coal, oil, and water power used by the human race. Allowing for inefficiencies in the manufacture of food, a very substantial increase in the world's output of energy would be required if such sources were to be used for food production. While the cost of such energy would perhaps be acceptable in wealthy countries, it would, by present standards, attach a minimum price tag to the food produced that would be too high to suit the needs of the poorer and hungrier nations who ought to be the first to benefit from artificial food.

For reasons discussed in the Appendix, the technological quest would be for new means of converting sunlight into chemical energy. These means would either be modelled on natural photosynthesis, the process in the green leaf in which an extremely complex sequence of reactions converts carbon dioxide into sugar, or they would use some quite different chemical reaction merely to "fix" the energy. Given concentrated energy in any suitable form, the possibility exists, in principle, for converting it into any other form. But one should not think too casually of such conversions: the capital costs of the facilities required for synthetic food production have to be given careful consideration.

The aim should be to make artificial "leaves" to collect solar energy, coupled to a food-making system of, say, 5 per cent average efficiency of primary production. If that could be realized, then one-hundredth of an acre of sunlight-collector would typically be sufficient to produce enough to provide a good diet of 3,000 calories a day for one person, of which 20 per cent would take the form of secondary animal products. This compares with a global average of one acre per head devoted to present agricultural production, which leaves most people with inadequate diets.

To obtain an impression of the areas of sunlight-collectors to be envisaged, if such efficiency can be obtained, we may note that less than one square mile would suffice for a town of 50,000 people; fifty million people in Britain could be fed using collectors equivalent in area to Westmorland. Similarly, the present 200 million Americans could be supported with an area smaller than Connecticut, a thousandth part of the inlying United States. The eventual world population of 9,000 million would call for 140,000 square miles of collector, or an area equivalent only to Italy, or Rhodesia, or Paraguay.

A more significant way of looking at this factor may be to observe that one-hundredth of an acre corresponds to a plot little more than twenty feet square. This is not very much more than the area per head taken up by a typical modern house in Britain and the United States. It suggests the possibility of decentralizing food production, with the roof of every house adapted to sunlight collection. As one acre of collector surface could support a hundred people, even Central London, with a population density of more than forty per acre, might find sufficient superficial area to be at least partly self-supporting.

What would the situation be if research failed to invent such an efficient sunlight-collecting system, or if it could be demonstrated that the system was theoretically impossible? The ambition of providing most of the world's food by compact artificial means would then have to be fulfilled, if at all, by the use of other energy supplies. If current exploration should yield reserves of oil and natural gas so far exceeding the requirements that one could count on a hundred years' supply adequate to make food for the growing population, as well as meeting the general energy needs, I believe that mankind would still be quite justified in making the switch from agriculture, in the confidence that rising standards of living during that coming century would enable it to afford more expensive sources of energy for food when the reserves were exhausted. Still leaving aside the hopes for nuclear fusion, conversion of sunlight by electrical means (as in solar cells) is demonstrably a sure, though currently an extremely expensive way, of obtaining all the energy we need.

If oil or natural gas is the starting material, the big initial problem of energy conversion is side-stepped (and with it, a source of inefficiency) and research can be directed to the secondary stages of changing already energetic material into palatable and nourishing form. In this connection, the pioneering work by British Petroleum, mentioned earlier, is a clear pointer to future possibilities.

Next to energy, the most important general question is of raw materials. Agriculture again sets a standard here by using materials of very low cost: carbon dioxide, oxygen and nitrogen from the air, and water and minerals present in the soil. Simple fertilizers are used nowadays, of course, to replace nitrogen and minerals removed from the soil by intensive harvesting, but a system of factory production of food cannot reasonably be based on anything much more costly.

Water supply presents difficulties in arid or over-populated areas, but it cannot be regarded seriously as an impediment to artificial food production, unless the methods evolved are unduly extravagant of water. It may prove possible to use sea water for at least some processes. Oxygen is plentiful and in any case, the crucial chemical steps in food synthesis involve getting rid of oxygen, rather than using it. The concentration of carbon dioxide in the air (only 0·03 per cent) is sufficient for growing plants although, as Dutch experiments have shown, there are benefits to be had from increasing the concentration of carbon dioxide in greenhouses. It is possible that some artificial methods will require higher concentrations of carbon dioxide: if physical concentration of the gas from the air, or its copious supply in the flues of coal- and oil-burning power stations do not serve, there is a vast amount locked up in the limestone rocks, from which it can be recovered quite easily—though only with the expenditure of energy, which costs money.

Nitrogen is a special case. Plants and animals used for food production in agriculture cannot "fix" the nitrogen from the air themselves. Nitrogen is an essential component of amino acids, and hence of protein, but it is chemically rather inert in its elementary gaseous form. We gulp it in and breathe it out unchanged. Natural plant communities and primitive agriculture depend on the activities of microbes in the soil and in the roots of certain plants to convert nitrogen into a suitable chemical form for assimilation and incorporation in the growing tissue of plants. In more advanced agriculture nitrogenous fertilizers are used to augment the natural supply; these are made from synthetic ammonia, produced from the nitrogen of the air by chemical rather than biological means. Even if biochemists cannot disentangle precisely how the nitrogen-fixing microbes do the trick at normal temperatures, nor the chemical engineers imitate it, as foreshadowed in Chapter 3, this chemical method, the Haber-Bosch process, ensures the supply of whatever fixed nitrogen is needed for food synthesis, at reasonable cost.

Important minerals used in agriculture, and also presumably in factory food, are phosphate and potash, which are mined. In addition, sulphur and a wide range of other elements figure in food; the provision of these in the required quantities presents no apparent difficulty. The extensive use of chemicals in agriculture has paved the way for wholly artificial methods.

Given energy supplies and raw materials, how might we elaborate the materials of food? There is still uncertainty about the eventual form of the primary energy conversion process, but exchanges of energy from one form into another can be contemplated. Many options are open to us on this side of the energy barrier.

METHODS OF CONVERSION

First, there is a whole range of possibilities employing living organisms or extracts from them. One could attempt to feed energetic chemical compounds in lieu of sunlight and carbon dioxide to plants or micro-organisms grown at high density in the dark, for human and animal foodstuffs. This would be the most straightforward way of acquiring the carbohydrates—sugars, starch, and perhaps roughage—in the form to which we are accustomed. Short of complete organisms, specialized organs or cells might be grown in large-scale cultures—milk-forming tissues, perhaps, or liver cells. Or one could isolate, using centrifuges, the sub-cellular units of plants and animals specifically responsible for elaborating the materials most needed in food—for example, the systems of the potato plant which form the starch of the potato itself, or the ribosomes of beef muscle cells which manufacture the protein of this tissue.

One apparent objection to the use of sub-cellular systems is the matter of renewal. All biological systems degenerate in time; in the living plant or animal they, or the cells or organisms of which they are "parts", are replaced; if sub-cellular systems are employed in food factories, would plants or animals have to be maintained to meet the demand for replacements? Perhaps, but tissue cultures could probably serve this purpose.

Tissue culture itself is one of the most attractive ideas for artificial food production. It is no longer far-fetched to think that we may learn how to grow beef-steak, for example, without a cow. Tissue culture, the technique for growing cells outside the organism from which they originated, is already used for special purposes in research and also for growing viruses in the manufacture of vaccine; the advent of polio vaccine depended on the successful cultivation of kidney cells. That in turn followed the introduction of antibiotics to preserve the cultures from the ravages of stray micro-organisms.

When cells are cultured by present techniques they tend to lose their specialized character. By deliberately letting specialized cells such as kidney or muscle revert to the undifferentiated nature of a newly fertilized egg, we can use them in a quite arbitrary way for a variety of synthetic purposes. If, on the other hand, we want to grow beef-steak we must simulate the conditions governing the growth and arrangement of the cells in the live animal, otherwise we shall finish up with something like finely divided mince.

Next comes a range of possibilities using the enzyme systems of plants, or artificial analogues, to promote the manufacture of key materials. At its simplest, this can be the use of a single enzyme to help with a single reaction; at a more complex stage it may be a series of enzymes or artificial equivalents to carry out the technically difficult, but naturally easy, process of building up glucose. The mechanism whereby green plants make glucose in the later stages of photosynthesis is quite well understood, but hard to imitate.

As for the purely chemical synthesis of nutritive chemicals, by measures owing nothing to nature, the present picture is mixed. The chemist cannot yet begin to rival living organisms in the production of glucose and other sugars. At least some vitamin manufacture remains a prerogative of natural systems. On the other hand, the Germans made some headway with the synthesis of fats from coal during the Second World War.

Making the full range of necessary amino acids and protein by chemical means would be fairly difficult. There has, however, been important progress recently, at least enough to suggest that we can envisage that one day this may seem economic sense. Already the simpler amino acids can be made industrially, and work at the General Electric Research Laboratory in the United States has shown how others can be made more easily than hitherto with good yields, by reacting glycine, the simplest amino acid, with isocyanates.

Here, as in carbohydrates produced by chemical means, there is a basic difference from living systems—that whereas the latter produce molecules with a particular left-handed "twist", the wholly artificial process usually creates equal numbers of right-handed and left-handed molecules. It is not too hard to separate them, but it may be necessary to do so should it turn out that the right-handed molecule is toxic. That could be the case if the animal or human machinery for protein synthesis is deceived into accepting right-handed molecules as raw material. If they are rejected, however, there may be no need to make the separation.

As for the "assembly" of amino acids into proteins, the Rockefeller Institute in New York has devised a system of using plastic beads to carry the growing chains of amino acids and has been able to make the whole process automatic. This is a laboratory technique, not an industrial process, but it shows how ingenuity can make operations which have previously seemed extremely awkward much more manageable.

In this and other ways chemists are learning to perform, by their own methods, syntheses that even a few years ago seemed almost hopeless to attempt outside living organisms. There is no doubt that, if synthesis of food were regarded as the prime object and research in this direction had adequate funds, new dodges would be found. From the viewpoint of present knowledge, however, it seems that the role of plain chemistry is likely to be limited to rather basic and simple steps in food production and that the elaboration of the complex, varied, and palatable materials we want to eat will best be done by living organisms or by chemical machinery isolated from them.

To demonstrate the ability of the chemical industry to make basic organic materials relevant to food production at interesting prices and using existing energy sources, it is worth quoting some figures given by David A. Shirley (*Organic Chemistry*, 1964). The price on the US market for the simplest carbohydrate, formaldehyde, CH_2O, is about three cents a lb (one cent is roughly a British penny). That for ethyl alcohol (industrial) is about six cents a lb. The simple nitrogenous organic material, urea, is made from carbon dioxide and ammonia under pressure to make a supplementary feed, replacing part of the protein requirements of cattle, at a cost of five cents a lb. Glycerol, on the other hand, a key component of fats and oils, is more expensive. It can be made from petroleum at a cost of about twenty-four cents a lb.

By way of summing up some of the possibilities here discussed, let us envisage what a food factory might be like.

Imagine, then, one designed to serve a population of 50,000 people. The principal source of energy is an array of chemical sunlight-collectors covering an area of 500 acres of a southward-facing slope. At ten-yard intervals down the slope, horizontal pipes pour out water containing a dark pigment and chemical reagents (we cannot yet specify these!). The dark water flows between two sheets of plastic for a few seconds, collecting light energy, before running into a collector where the primary chemical reaction proceeds to completion.

The water is then pumped into a tank containing a mass of microscopic plants growing under high-pressure carbon dioxide. The carbon dioxide comes from an oil-burning power station. The plants are not functioning as sunlight-collectors, but as chemical systems for using the activated liquid and the carbon dioxide to grow very rapidly, elaborating carbohydrate and protein. At the far side of the tank, part of the water filters out—still containing pigment and reagents but now depleted of its energy; more water is added to make up for that absorbed by the growing plants and it goes back to the sunlight-collector. In each carbon-dioxide tank, serving two and a half acres of collector, the plants grow at a rate of about a ton a day. The tanks are emptied each night, leaving "seed" material for the following day.

The array of 200 collectors and their associated tanks are under the control of a computer, which compares the rate of growth in each tank with the prevailing daylight intensity. Any discrepancy from the expected output of a tank sets in train an automatic check that all the machinery is working correctly. If it is, the change in output is taken as a sign of infection—the biggest hazard for this form of food production. A foreign organism or virus, or occasionally a mutant form of the cultivated plant, may intrude to exploit the hyper-fertile conditions of the system. If it is not promptly dealt with, by emptying the tank in question, destroying its contents and cleaning it out, the infection could spread all over the hillside. As the destruction proceeds, again automatically, a sample of the suspect material is despatched to a laboratory for diagnosis.

The plant material produced each day is used in a variety of ways; each tank serves a specific purpose and there are differences in the species and varieties of microscopic plants grown. Part is turned into a white flour. Part is broken up to provide oils, carbohydrates, and proteins for subsequent diverse manufacturing processes. Part is used for growing yeast, as a very cheap source of rich protein. And part—about two-fifths—is converted into animal protein.

Three main production lines for animal protein operate side by side. In one, cattle, pigs, and poultry are raised on the plant material to provide high-grade meat and eggs. In another, milk is formed continuously by a culture of milk-producing glands; it is intended both for drinking and for the making of butter and cheese. In the third, beef muscle grows continuously in long tubes, extruding itself for chopping into steak-like portions. A complex of small works turns out a selection of prepared foods—soups, sausages, bread, beer, and so on—but these are for national or regional distribution. Vitamins and flavours, coming from national suppliers, are added as required.

To fill the big gap left by the absence of fruit and vegetables, various devices are used. Orange and lemon juice
is produced from cultures of the relevant parts of those
fruits. Chemical processing of the primary plant material
produces fibrous material with some "bite" to it. But, for
the most part, those who want fruit and vegetables for
aesthetic reasons (there is no nutritional necessity for
them) obtain them from their own gardens or from such
market gardeners and fruit growers as still function.

Is the food from our hypothetical factory dull? Not
necessarily. Flavours and textures are fully under chemical
control and a wide range of choice is possible. Most of the
traditional contents of the larder are retained in one form
or another; the chief departure for those who do not want
to spend the extra money on "real" vegetables is that
"meat and two veg" would tend to be replaced by
Italian-type pastas and meat sauce, or similar combinations of meat and carbohydrate.

For the very poor, combinations of plant and yeast
material, reinforced with vitamins, will provide an admit-
tedly dull, but completely nutritious basic food. The
important aim, with world hunger in mind, is to go by
the shortest and most economical route to nutritionally
adequate foods. Only then should we seek to introduce
variety by devices of the kind I have mentioned.

TOWARDS A PROGRAMME

How much research being done today is relevant to these
goals of artificial photosynthesis and food production?
Scientists have speculated about the possibilities (see
Preface, pp. 12–14) but it cannot be said that the goals

have been made particularly explicit in current research programmes. Progressive chemical and pharmaceutical companies, and even some food manufacturers, are alert to the possibilities, but they do not say very much about them. I have mentioned a few specific developments in the course of this chapter, but even these are not getting to the heart of the matter.

On the other hand, there is a tremendous volume of research that has a strong bearing on these possible revolutionary developments. Understanding of the natural mechanisms of photosynthesis is advancing rapidly, chiefly as a result of work in the United States. Molecular biology, pioneered in Britain, has opened the blinds to a comprehensive view of how the overall government of cells is effected, particularly in the synthesis of enzymes and other proteins. The somewhat older science of biochemistry, which interlocks with molecular biology and is primarily concerned with the complex sequences of enzyme reactions in living systems, has elucidated several of the vital processes. On the energy-production side, photochemistry is giving us a broad knowledge of chemical reactions induced by electromagnetic energy, while a more sophisticated form of thermodynamics has been produced to deal with the peculiarities of energy manipulations in living systems. General organic chemistry is becoming ever more clever in its synthetic methods, while chemical engineering, too, becomes subtler, more versatile, and more efficient. A range of new techniques has been moving out of the laboratory into the chemical plant, for promoting or monitoring reactions, and others are following; in particular, it is worth mentioning that chromatography, the powerful analytical tool which separates different materials by their different rates of movement through a system, should be adaptable to industrial production and may be relevant to artificial food production.

Nutritionists are narrowing down the precise food requirements of man, in chemical terms. Food technologists have built up their skills in manipulating the flavours and textures of materials. A notable example is the widespread use of an amino acid, glutamic acid, to impart a "meaty" flavour to many products. Techniques of tissue culture are under constant development for pharmaceutical and research purposes. Microbiologists have a large and growing knowledge of how to culture microorganisms of all kinds, and of the scope of the repertoire of these species, in respect both of what they can metabolize and what they can make. More specifically, the para-agricultural technique of growing microscopic aquatic plants for food is a subject of continuing research.

Can all these threads of research be woven into a large-scale, co-ordinated programme for food manufacture? Certainly, if the effort were well supported by research funds and the objectives were clear, we might achieve the desired end result more rapidly, by analogy with "crash" programmes like radar, the atomic bomb, and space technology. But that would depend on getting the brightest scientists involved and experience suggests that they dislike big programmes except in times of war. There are good professional reasons for this: a big programme requires planning, an identification of routes, preconceptions about the means to the end. This is very different from the free-range imaginative, opportunistic character of the most revolutionary research.

What is probably more important is that the desirability and importance of artificial methods of food production should be more clearly articulated, by scientists and by national leaders (herein is a prime motive for this book). If the main aim, and possible courses to it, are kept in mind by a wide range of scientists; if some groups are set up to attempt to develop practical techniques drawing on available knowledge and ideas; and if governments are prepared to reinforce success in this field—then, I think, the possibilities will develop quickly enough.

There is one activity in which the artificial production of food already looms as a decisive problem—and that is space exploration. If men really are to reach the planets, in journeys taking months or years, they will have to produce their own food as they go along: otherwise the weight of food will be penalizing. They may carry nuclear reactors aboard, or catch the energy of sunlight, but either way they will have to rely upon essentially non-agricultural techniques. Accordingly there are serious studies of cultivation of micro-organisms, of energy conversion, of food elaboration, and of recovery of waste material, in the highly artificial environment of a space ship. These are closely connected with the need to maintain a breathable supply of air and eliminate noxious substances in the environment.

The constraints about costs of equipment and energy supplies that loom large in artificial food production for the general population on Earth do not apply to spacecraft. But the techniques developed may be of the utmost relevance to terrestrial systems. Thus we may yet see a pleasing paradox. Space operations have been widely condemned for their seeming irrelevancy to the problems of a hungry and impoverished world. With the advent of meteorological and communications satellites, that argument is weakened. If the almost incidental matter of feeding the astronaut should lead to the development of techniques for freeing man from the labour of agriculture, the whole bizarre manned space business will have given adequate return on that score alone.

Two further fields of research necessary for this programme are: (1) prolonged biological testing of synthetic foods in animals and subsequently in human volunteers, to make quite sure that they represent no hazards to health; and (2) augmented research into the social aspects of nutrition, from the viewpoint of acceptability of new food products. In the latter field, food manufacturers in the advanced countries have demonstrated that novel products can indeed be sold, if they are attractive and well publicized. While at an intermediate stage consumer conservatism may delay the full exploitation of synthetic food, in my belief it need not do so for long.

There may always be aesthetic reasons for preferring "real" bread and "real" milk. In an increasingly affluent world, many will be able to afford them, and there will doubtless be farmers ready to supply them. All that matters for my general argument is that most of the food for most of the people should be made with comparatively high efficiency of utilization of energy, and that the yields per acre from surviving farms should conform to the best present-day standards. Then we can face the prospect of a doubled or trebled population with some equanimity. Not only should food supplies be assured, but a great deal of land will be released to enable us to spread ourselves and to reconstruct the face of the Earth.

(*See also* Appendix to this chapter, p. 227.)

CHAPTER 7

A Change in the Rules

THERE ARE at least three very different ways of making plans for the future. One is to construct a Utopia, visualizing an end result that embodies some features thought to be desirable. It need not be particularly comprehensive; indeed it seldom is. "Wouldn't it be nice if . . ." is the form of construction here. Wouldn't it be nice if we could dispense with private property, or with congenital stupidity; wouldn't it be nice if we had world government, or if we spread our civilization throughout the solar system; and so on. To be interesting, Utopia-builders have to envisage something remote from prevailing conditions and frequently the practical means of achieving it are obscure. Utopias are useful to the rest of us for taking compass bearings, in order to gauge our directions of change at the present time, just as a sailor may plot his course from islands he never expects to visit. The trouble with Utopias is that they are usually at once revolutionary and, to their adherents, noble—precisely the kind of thing that has caused the world so much trouble in imperialistic, religious, and revolutionary wars and in the major and minor atrocities committed in the name of ideals.

At the other extreme, in the methods of planning for the future, is sheer opportunism. Here there is little sense of direction except national or personal aggrandizement, little thought of motive except response to opportunity or threat. The material or knowledge to be exploited is already to hand, so one makes a treaty or an atomic bomb, a motorway or a colour television system, or whatever it may be, without any coherent scheme for thereby changing the world—but changing it all the same and in practice more profoundly than dreams of Utopia do. Chapter 4 gave an impression of some technical possibilities existing for the opportunist.

Between these two approaches to the future—ends in search of means or means in search of ends—there is a third, problem-solving. In contrast with the Utopia-builder, the problem-solver's aims are limited; they are also usually negative—to tackle juvenile delinquency, to get rid of air pollution, to cure disease, and the like. Unlike the opportunist, the problem-solver does not necessarily have the means to hand. He may have to undertake research or invention, or wage a long persuasive battle, or compromise with conflicting interests. Problem-solving is the essence of Fabian gradualism, of government by committee, of proscriptive legislation. By and large, if you are a problem-solver you let things develop on opportunistic or quasi-utopian lines and then you sort out the dislocations, the side-effects, the failures, in order to minimize obvious social evils. You have to chart your course for short periods, but you do so pragmatically. You know how things ought not to be (drawing on conventional moral codes) but you are very vague about how they should be.

"Problems", as any reading of serious journalism will show, are the obsession of contemporary liberal thought. Equally, the scientist and technologist are preoccupied with "problems" of a more technical kind. The two groups swap problems. While the government demands technical innovation to increase the gross national product, in order that its problem-solving social programme can go through, it wrestles diplomatically with proliferation of nuclear weapons invented by the scientists. Scientists are more efficient problem-solvers than politicians are, but their solutions tend to create new problems of a social or technical kind.

We owe a lot to the problem-solvers, but they have never given us much sense of direction or of purpose. Of course hunger, disease, illiteracy, tyranny, etc., are evils; of course the world would be better without them. But, supposing the wars against them succeed, how are the resulting well-fed, healthy, highly educated, free people going to live?

To a first approximation, the problems facing us are clearly so immense and self-evidently in need of solution if people are going to lead even tolerable lives, that there is plenty to keep the present generation busy and well-oriented without looking beyond the day of victory. Such a pragmatic view is very tempting. "Let our grandchildren decide how they ought to live, when we have given them the chance to choose." But I for one have changed my mind and for more than one reason. There will be no end to the "problems" and if men are to excuse themselves indefinitely from thinking outside a narrow range of obsessional topics they will slide into opportunistic ways. More practically, the routes to the solution of various problems are diverse and we have to make choices; unless we have ways of judging alternative means to one end, or alternative ends of one means, we shall blunder. Problem-solving can now draw on the new techniques for dealing with complex systems (described in Chapter 5) and it will become possible for us to take more elements into account. We can begin to cope with the rich complexity of human life; but that means adopting attitudes about many other things besides the narrow definition of the "problem".

An example will help to make my meaning plainer. A common utopian ideal is that every person should be educated to the limits of his interest and capacity. In literal terms, this means that there should be more places in institutions of higher education than there are potential students to fill them. The opportunistic politician may not aim quite so high as that, but he supposes a close correlation between education and his nation's military and economic strength and so decides on bold programmes of school and university expansion. Somebody points out that education is a complex dynamic system with plenty of chance of dislocation, so problem-solvers like Lord Robbins' committee in Britain are called in to help with the planning. Everything for once seems fine with everyone swimming the same way. But in fact several basic questions remain unanswered—dangerously so, when we consider that what we are doing now will determine the pattern of academic life into the twenty-first century. For example:

(1) At what stage will the process of expansion slow down or stop? This is critical, because when growth is arrested the academic world will tend to "freeze" in whatever the prevailing pattern may be at that time.

(2) For what vocational and leisure interests in the twenty-first century is the educational system providing?

(3) Is it right to embark on such programmes without questioning current academic assumptions about the proper content and methods of education?

I shall not digress to offer answers to these questions; my purpose is simply to illustrate the inadequacy of all three of the main methods of coping with the future. The utopian may be simply delighted with the quantitative expansion of education, but he will find, unless he attends to these practical questions, that the result is less brilliant than he expects. The opportunist is not looking more than a few years ahead anyway. The problem-solvers will respond all right, when these questions have converted themselves into "problems", but by then their solutions will be of necessity makeshift.

From the character of these unanswered questions we can see what is missing in the usual approaches to the future. It is simply the comprehensive view—that which sees education, or whatever else is under study, as a process in the midst of other processes, and seeks a harmony between them all.

This quest for harmony is utopian, in the sense that it is informed by a belief that if the manifold activities of man, and of nature too, can be better integrated, the Earth will be a safer and more congenial planet. But apart from that it knows no glib formula for the ideal society. Just as a composer of music works with the instruments available to him, and is willing to find a place for new ones as they appear, so the composer of themes for the future should take the old elements with the new and try to orchestrate them.

The composer can work with utopian ideals and evaluate them coolly; he can spot the same short-term possibilities as the opportunist; he must be something of a problem-solver, or at least be able to guess which problems are soluble and along what lines. But he is more than a critic; he has to see possible new patterns and explore them. He must do so quite humbly, and resist any temptation to over-simplify or to promote a possible scheme to an exalted place. A glance around the world shows many viable patterns of life which are, in theory, mutually contradictory. However attractive a scheme may be to its inventor, there is nearly always another way of achieving the same end result—and the end result itself may not be indispensable, or even, on broader reflection, desirable.

For the composer, no system is so necessarily and sufficiently good as to make its fulfilment "essential". Nuclear weapons, for example, are rightly abhorred, and rational men have doubted whether the human race can survive for long unless it destroys its stockpiles of those weapons. It might therefore be deduced that such a course is essential. In that case should we be prepared to go to any lengths to bring it about: even to war, if need be, since the survival of the species is said to depend on it? But a major war today will involve the use of thermonuclear weapons—so it turns out that the destruction of nuclear weapons is not, after all, essential, although it may still be highly desirable.

Does this broad-minded attitude mean that the composer will be amoral, or poorly motivated, or deficient in opinions of his own? No more than a composer of music is tone-deaf, or uninspired, or unexpressive because he is not playing the instruments himself. The quest for harmony between such elements as the Indonesian village and the American moon rocket range, solar energy and wild life, urban transport and public health, the individual and his computerized environment—here is a powerful and modern kind of morality in its own right. Motivation in plenty is to be found in the dissonances of everyday life, and in the glimpses of better things that we have when schemes go rather well—in the Tennessee Valley, the creation of safe world-wide air services, the National Health Service in Britain, and so on.

The would-be composer, looking at the present and at the years ahead is, however, obliged to adopt a somewhat utopian stance. This is not of his own choosing: he is obliged to do so by the character and pace of current changes. He is forced to believe that the world in the twenty-first century will be radically different, in one of a great number of possible patterns. Unless he tries to select one—which is uncomfortably like prescribing a Utopia—his task becomes unmanageable. And to make this choice, he is forced, like the Utopia-builder, to look again at the basic assumptions about human society. Nevertheless, he may strive for objectivity and beware of glib solutions.

Accordingly, before attempting to compose a possible future, we must explore the revolutionary, quasi-utopian consequences of the most noteworthy single result of current science: through automation, long life, and population growth, a great many people are going to have a great deal of time on their hands.

The redundancies of automation in manufacturing industry can, of course, only be enlarged by artificial, computer-controlled methods of food production. In a narrow, technical sense the prospect is of large-scale unemployment throughout the world—unless, that is, consumption of goods and services increases to impossible heights. It might be thought that the need to make up the back-log of under-privilege in the developing countries will consume a vast amount of human labour indefinitely, but in fact, of course, there is an inherent contradiction in the idea of building up a high universal standard of living on a basis of cheap labour. If large numbers of well-paid workers were to be employed to do work that should, technically, be done by machines, the products would be inferior and expensive. Suppliers of plant to under-developed countries are asked to cut out the automatic frills and provide for the employment of as many people as possible: often the answer is that it cannot be done. A modern petroleum refinery literally would not work without its automatic controls. Similarly, it is almost certain that synthetic food will be produced with minimal labour force. The need to keep physical conditions just so, and (perhaps even more important) the need for strict hygiene, will see to that.

In physics and engineering there are plenty of systems called "bi-stable". A simple example is a bicycle at rest, which will fall on to one side or on to the other. Others are the magnets used as memory stores in electronic computers, and the electrical system of the nerves, which ensures that they are either at rest or transmitting signal "spikes" of a rather precisely defined voltage. In matters of prosperity, the technical and economic systems we know tend to be bi-stable: either a nation is poor, and in perpetual danger of growing poorer, or it is rich and liable to grow richer. There are, of course, transitional states, but these do not last long; most nations today fall clearly into one group or the other.

It would doubtless be possible to find a combination of technologies that would enable a nation to stabilize at an intermediate level of prosperity, but such a programme would be bizarre and would probably not remain for long acceptable to the population concerned. Broadly speaking, then, poor nations have to try to leap into the class of rich nations, and to accept the prevailing manufacturing methods of the rich nations. And these are at present on the high road to automation, with the consequent "hazard" of technological unemployment.

Unemployment has earned a terrible name for itself because of its association both with poverty and with loss of dignity. Somehow, we have to stand the notion on its head, and draw a rough equation between the unemployed common man and the "gentleman of leisure" of Edwardian England. But to do so requires a radical reconsideration of what human life is all about. So we are forced by our scheme and time-scale to look beyond the technical and economic issues to social and political ones. It then becomes clear that we have to invent a new kind of state.

We can duck the issue for quite a while, if we choose to do so. That is to say, we can preserve the illusion of work indefinitely, with each man having "a job" by such devices as:

(1) Lengthening the unproductive years by longer education and earlier retirement.

(2) Shortening the working day or week ("the five-day week-end").

(3) Cultivation of obsolescence and waste, to increase consumption.

(4) The invention of new work, such as space exploration.

(5) The growth of non-material occupations, such as scholarship and scientific research.

(6) Parkinson's Law, which is by no means a joke but a shrewd observation of human behaviour in expanding work unnecessarily to fill the time available for its completion.

Indeed, we shall have to make use of all these things if we do not first reconstruct our ideas to cope with the new "leisured" existence and to eradicate the idea of the importance of work which has dogged us since the invention of agriculture. But it seems silly to pass up the opportunity for thinking afresh and, in any case, it is at least plausible that we have another bi-stable situation—that there is no stability to be found at a point intermediate between the work-dominated and the leisure-oriented society. In the high crime, suicide, and divorce rates of the affluent nations we can see signs of instability.

Well-meaning attempts to face these problems lay emphasis on education, on youth clubs, on cultural pursuits, on organized facilities for games, and so on. To suggest that nothing short of a major reconstruction of our way of life is needed to defeat the boredom of leisured affluence may seem pessimistic to conservative minds; and to go on to propose that we have to treat life as a huge game may strike as absurd or monstrous the more radically-minded people who tend in a puritanical sense to be conservative.

But I use the word "game" advisedly. By a quirk of derivation, the English use that term both for a recreation and for hunted animals. If we stick firmly to the notion that man is by evolutionary design a hunter, we may be able to discover how we should live.

It is no pun or idle metaphor to see social institutions such as have existed since the dawn of agriculture as an elaborate game, the prizes of which are individual wealth and power. Constitutions and laws are the rules of the game, and one ploy is to seek to change the rules to one's own advantage. Intelligence, money, and force, and alliances of these, constitute the chief counters in the game, but the rules are biased in favour of those who are already winning and, as the winners are also in a much better position to cheat, most people at most times have been losers.

Until comparatively recently in what are now the advanced countries, the game was of a kind technically known to games theorists as a "zero-sum game": that means, what one man won another man lost, because the per capita wealth and power available for distribution as prizes was scarcely affected by the course of play. Trade helped, of course, and conquest could enlarge the share of one country, including the poor of that country, at the expense of others, but globally the sum remained substantially constant, or at least increased too slowly to benefit the losers much. Only when a side-game started, as a recreation for gentlemen—the game of science—was the general game of the world transformed into a non-zero-sum game, so that even the losers in Britain today are in many material respects far better off than the Plantagenet kings. Of course, the rules have also been changed in favour of the losers, because of the demands of modern industry for well-educated, healthy, enterprising workers and because the winners can only keep on winning if the workers buy their own products.

But now the game is taking a new (and sinister) turn, well exposed by Michael Young in his *Rise of the Meritocracy* (Thames & Hudson, 1958). The ascendancy allowed by the rules, first to force and then to money, is now being transferred to intelligence. It is potentially the most dangerous because it is both more plausible and more self-confident. The running of a complex modern state does seem to require cultivated intelligences. So we have an educational system designed to identify the brightest youngsters, irrespective of origin, and groom them for authority over their less intelligent brothers and sisters. It is "fairer" in a narrow class sense; at the level of the individual, however, being born with a high or low IQ is as much a matter of chance as being born in a palace or a slum. The closest precedent was in the administration of the medieval Church, which took bright youngsters to be monks; its results did not suggest that intelligent power is a guarantee either of humane or of progressive rule.

The warrior, the money-lender, and the master of arts have all been glorified in turn, and the last goes today to join the descendants of the others on the benches of the House of Lords. Yet between them they represent only the preoccupations of various eras, and nothing like a full spectrum of the human virtues.

Fortunately, the potential tyranny of intelligence can be nipped in the bud. The computer is the means of doing so. Early impressions of the computer have created the idea that only the most intelligent people can use it, but if this was ever true it is certainly no longer the case. A lot of brain-power goes into devising the machinery and the programmes, of course, but thereafter anyone capable of typing a coherent sentence can converse directly with the computer. That limited form of intelligence which is needed for managing complex affairs along a prescribed course is provided in ample measure by an interaction of machine and ordinary men; confronted with the instant logic and organizing ability of the computer, variations in human intelligence are of vanishing significance at the operating level.

It turns out, indeed, that the three most valued skills of the old game—military, entrepreneurial, and intellectual—are all devalued by recent technological advances; that is, by weapons that are too powerful to use, by techniques of high productivity that could create material wealth up to the limits of natural resources, and by the computer as an aid to thought.

The changing situation is hard to grasp, or to credit, because present circumstances have intensified the old game. The world spends more than $100,000 million a year on defence. The attempt of all nations to maximize their wealth in a highly competitive, fast-moving technological situation makes the enterprising deployment of money a matter of direct concern of governments. And the demand for intellectual ability, especially in science and technology, has become so great that the "brain drain" towards the most advanced centres is seriously endangering balanced world development. Nevertheless, these are the last frantic phases of the old game, as conducted by men who still see it as a zero-sum game in which the object is to do the other fellow down or at least to stop him doing you down.

The only peaceful outcome must be such that everyone becomes rich. Then the old game will be seen to be futile and dangerous, and the first, orientating question for the composer is, what new game will take its place?

Let there be no mistake about it—a game there must be. Human and material resources have to be deployed according to some set of rules. Men want a sense of purpose in their lives, something they know they must do when they get up in the morning, and a means of measuring their achievement by some objective criterion at the end of the day. Even anarchistic ideals, in which the aim is to minimize authority by some men over others, have their own quite complex sets of rules according to which the game is to be played. So while, by talking of "games", we recognize the ephemeral character of social institutions that seem obsessively indispensable to those in the thick of the old game, we need not be cynical in our use of the word.

The composer has to cast around in his imagination to identify possible games, and choose one which seems plausible for adoption and also, in essence, capable of harmonizing a very wide range of environmental, social, and personal elements. Let us therefore set down, in comparable form, the chief characteristics of past, present, and some possible future games.

(1) *Palaeolithic game.* This game was played by small groups of men and consisted in finding food, principally by hunting. Rewards for success were survival, feasts, honour, and time to develop culturally. It was in practice usually a non-zero-sum game, because of the low population density; but it became a zero-sum game locally where food on the hoof was scarce, forcing the eventual pioneering of agriculture. The Palaeolithic game would not be feasible today, because the extremely large human population could not be sustained by wild life.

(2) *Neolithic/present-day game* (what I have called the "old game"). This game, played by individuals, organizations, and nations, consists in the manipulation of monetary wealth and human power, in order to maximize them, for these are themselves the rewards of the game. Until the scientific revolution it was for most practical purposes a zero-sum game, but it now becomes obsolescent and dangerous because wealth and social and military power can be created almost without limit.

(3) *A modified money game.* This would be an attempt to alter the rules of the present-day game, to turn it back into something more nearly a zero-sum game while circumscribing the possible upper and lower limits of

wealth and power. One possibility is to cultivate the collection of money for its own sake, with heavy taxes on
spending, while paying highly (if mainly symbolically)
for socially desirable activities. The game is played
roughly as at present but the object is to maximize
savings, for which one is honoured. Personal power might
have to be paid for—a sink rather than a source of wealth.
Economically this is in the category of zero-sum games,
but it can look like a non-zero-sum game if unlimited
inflation is permitted.

(4) *A gambling game.* Here man's chief preoccupation
would be continual redistribution of wealth and honour
by chance. The game is played by individuals or by
syndicates. By the use of computers the game can be made
fast, tense, and constantly absorbing, with built-in safe-
guards against ruin. Players are honoured for their luck.
It is a zero-sum game if the wealth available for redistribution is limited, but the biggest prizes could be very large.

(5) *A simulated-skills game.* This would be a game played
on computers by individuals for financial reward, but
unlike the gambling game would depend entirely on skill.
Each competitor might have to carry out one simulated
task a day, such as flying an aeroplane by remote control,
or shooting at moving targets, or examining a criminal
suspect, or painting a portrait, and he might be paid for
success or penalized for serious failure. It might be possible to incorporate real tasks into this game, so that the
player would never know whether the aeroplane or the
criminal he is presented with is real or not. In so far as it
is mainly unproductive, this is a zero-sum game.

(6) *A miscellaneous-tasks game.* In this case, the tasks are
mainly real. The computer would arbitrarily allocate a
task to each competitor for a stated period (let us say a

month): this task might be cargo-handling, for example, or stage-management, or baby care. The competitor would travel to the appropriate centre, he would be trained, he would carry out the task and he would be judged. If he did well he would be given a trophy and a bonus payment; if he failed badly he would have to repeat the task once. The object of the game would be to collect as many trophies as possible; although the tasks chosen might tend to create fresh wealth, it could perhaps be regarded as a deliberately inefficient non-zero-sum game.

(7) *A sports game.* If the present-day sports "industry" were expanded to embrace, as participants, a much larger section of the population, it could become the principal occupation for men. Played by individuals and teams, and exploiting all the traditional and new sporting activities, from chess to water polo, this game's system of rewards and honours is already well established and in part professionalized. In many ways it would be one of the easiest games to establish, starting as it would from our present customs. It is a zero-sum game, except in the very limited sense that athletic records can be broken.

(8) *A sex game.* Here the preoccupation is the pursuit of sleeping partners, and promiscuity is honoured. In some communities this is already a traditional game, although one may doubt whether it can be regarded as a life-time's activity by any but the most dedicated; and it is difficult to reconcile it with the care of young children. It could, however, develop more "officially" for young adults before marriage. Without control both of conception and of venereal disease it would, of course, be a negative-sum game.

(9) *A ritual game.* This is a game, again traditional, played by human groups, in which the object is to create

mutual satisfaction by elaborate behaviour and to win honour by excellent execution. Much unproductive time can be passed in celebration of birth, graduation, marriage, and death, seasonal festivities, anniversaries—even of sunrise and sunset. New rituals introduced by television include the daily perusal of the weather charts by the gravely watching millions, and the guesses by a jury of the likelihood of commercial success for new pop-records. In this connection, it is amusing to speculate on the possibility of programming a computer to be a god—a jealous, Old Testament kind of god, requiring constant appeasement by meticulous ritual to prevent spectacular displays of impatience, but giving unpredictable rewards in the form of information, advice, or even cash hand-outs.

(10) *An entertainment game.* Yet another present-day activity which could be promoted to supreme status is the entertainment industry. With most of mankind taking part, the aim would be to achieve increased reward and honour by applauded contributions of one kind or another. A non-zero-sum game, limited only by the available talent and by audience satiation.

(11) *A knowledge game.* By elevating the acquisition of knowledge to be the chief aim of mankind, a game could be set up based on the rules and customs of the academic world. The aim would be either to *learn* or to *discover*, and success in both would be rewarded and honoured. Practical skills would count as well as book-learning; the world would be, as it were, one big university, with research as its principal occupation. Plainly, intelligence would be an advantage for such a system, but it need not be disproportionately so. It is a non-zero-sum game, with unlimited scope for extending achievement in the natural and social sciences, and in the arts.

(12) *A "big science" game*. This would be a more indus-trialized version of the knowledge game, in which the dominant activities would be those such as the coloniza-tion of the oceans and the solar system, the attempt to communicate with the planets of other stars, exploration of the Earth's interior and costly experimentation such as is taking place in high-energy physics today. The aim for the individual might be to work on such projects in a high or a low capacity for rewards of wealth and honour distributed perhaps according to conventional ideas. As most of the projects suggested here are unproductive in the immediate sense, while the reward system is conven-tional, it must be regarded as a zero-sum game.

(13) *A beautification game*. Here the aim would be the creation of aesthetically delightful surroundings. Indi-viduals, organizations, and nations could play the game, through architecture, the arts, and landscaping, and rewards might take the form of prizes and (less impor-tantly) of tourist revenues. Continuous reshaping of the environment could be made possible by efficient and cheap methods of construction, and all the arts would be fully exercised in embellishing it. It would be literally a zero-sum game if the rewards were limited, but in practice its pursuit would be its own reward.

(14) *A conservation game*. In this the aim would be the safekeeping of the natural environment, possibly com-bined with maximum economy in the use of scarce materials. The individual and the community might be allocated responsibility for a given tract of land or sea, which they would have to study and manage in order to optimize the natural biological productivity. The rewards would be prizes and the by-products of the conservation activities—most notably the opportunity for hunting. If

conserved natural wealth is regarded as an economic asset, it is a non-zero-sum game.

(15) *An environment game.* The last four games, numbers 11 to 14, are largely complementary or at least mutually compatible. It is therefore possible to conceive of a broader game, of which the overall purpose is to enhance, by the efforts of the individual and his community, the individual's own knowledge and enjoyment of the terrestrial environment, natural and human. The aim would be to manipulate non-monetary wealth and human knowledge in order to maximize them, for these are themselves the rewards of the game. It is a non-zero-sum game, limited only by the capacity of the human mind.

I hope that these examples of games serve at least to illustrate that there is great scope for game-making. Before any new game is adopted, however, there ought to be a major investigation by the social sciences. While a theory of game preferences could draw on archaeology and anthropology, and on history and psychology, experimental studies of games using smallish groups of people would be much more convincing. It is often suggested that the "human sciences" can do little in the way of experiments. That is true only because of the earnest belief that the present organization of society is something more than a game. It is my hunch that, despite the opportunities of complex-systems analysis discussed in Chapter 5, the social sciences can achieve a stature comparable with the natural sciences when, and only when, their frame of reference is enlarged to an infinite universe of possible human interactions and when the social scientists boldly start setting up game-like experiments with human volunteers.

In time, no doubt, the chief concern of political theory,

too, will be with the merits of rival systems of games, in contrast with the present tinkering with the institutional rules of an obsolescent game. Of course, if the sources of political strength lie in attainment within the prevailing game, as at present, and particularly if many countries in the world have adopted the same game, there will be built-in conservatism to prevent erratic changes. But recognizing the arbitrary nature of the choice of game should be a safeguard against excessive zeal in defence of it.

For present purposes, the composer has to make some choice of game, in anticipation of the detailed researches and debate that are really necessary. This is the quasi-utopian decision I mentioned earlier, and he has to allow himself to be influenced by particular social aims and technical possibilities. He must also make value judgements about the games in principle available. He may think, for example, that of those listed above, numbers 3 to 6 are too artificial or unambitious, while sport, sex, ritual, and entertainment (numbers 7 to 10) should properly remain auxiliary activities for those so disposed, rather than the arbiters of human achievement.

It is among numbers 11 to 15 that the most purposeful activities (by present-day standards) are to be found and, because of its breadth, the choice for human society's main game should properly fall on number 15—provided, that is, that the supreme importance of the "environment" can be made plausible and absorbing enough for the majority of mankind.

In anticipation of this choice, the "rules" of the *environment game* (number 15) were worded to match those of the old game (number 2). It will be seen that there is a simple substitution of "non-monetary wealth and human knowledge" for "monetary wealth and human power", for both the instruments and the rewards of the game.

By non-monetary wealth I mean both the things that money can buy and the things it cannot buy, in contrast with cash in the bank. It includes all the marketable paraphernalia and services of our present civilization, which will be kept in abundance, if automation performs as expected. It includes food—provided, for present purposes, mainly by synthetic means. It also includes, however, climate, companionship, recreational opportunities and, most valuable of all in the twenty-first century, generous living-space. Such things should be entirely acceptable in preference to money. I do not mean that money itself has to disappear, if it is convenient to retain it for purposes of trade or allocation of wealth: only that much more importance will be attached to non-monetary rewards than is the case today.

To see the concept more clearly, consider it from the viewpoint of an undistinguished individual. Today he knows that he has to "earn a living" by finding work for which he will be paid; that is the game. In the environment game he is expected to "address himself to a living" as a highly trained and diligent gamekeeper (this term is used as shorthand for a more elaborate scheme of activities to be explored in the next chapter).

If he is prepared to do so, the rewards of the game are largely in kind. He has the rights to enjoy the countryside, to use the community's vehicles and research facilities, to participate in the government of the environment, to hunt. Whatever his talents may be, he has the opportunity to win distinction by skill and good sense, and thereby to acquire special privileges—a seat of honour perhaps, a home with a special view over the countryside, additional hunting rights, or a private laboratory.

Failure to "play the game" may penalize him in that, while he and his family will be maintained in reasonable health and comfort regardless, and he will have ordinary democratic rights as a citizen, he will have no status or privileges in the environment game. He will be virtually a prisoner in his town, because unless he is prepared to act in accordance with the rules he will not be allowed into the countryside. If he travels, he may find himself unwelcome in other places, when he is asked about his part in the game.

Plainly, such a system is capable of endless variation and refinement, from one community to another. New political and social traditions would have to be developed to reinforce the notion that care of the environment is the most important function of social life and to breed conviction that the game must be taken seriously. But while the social modes would provide great scope for argument, once the broad principle of the environment game has been accepted it could provide a stable basis for a completely new way of life, in which the local variations would be of no more than local interest.

Present-day conservation activities are properly subject to endless compromise in deference to the needs of man. Unless a valley is flooded a city may die of thirst; unless a new tract of land is put under the plough, men may die of hunger; unless dilute radioactivity can be released into the sea, nuclear energy cannot be economically developed; unless new housing estates are built, city slums cannot be cleared; unless power-lines are strung over the countryside industrial progress is endangered. Even in the great national parks of Africa, human considerations such as tourism assume great importance. Almost everywhere the conservationists are on the defensive.

Men's apparent helplessness to do anything much about protecting their environment is, of course, basically absurd. In our current scale of values we can only assess the worth of pleasant countryside or elegant cities by the very crude indicators of land prices and tourist revenue. In the present-day game, the environment comes low among the priorities.

Only with a radical alteration of the rules of the game, to make the enjoyment of a pleasing environment as coveted as money and material goods are today, is there any hope at all that two or three times as many people can live on this planet without defacing it irretrievably.

One way of interpreting what follows in the next chapter, in our elaboration of the environment game, is to say that we must rediscover our own planet as conscientiously and with the same sense of wonder as we are now preparing to explore Mars and the other planets of the solar system. Just as the engineers of the forthcoming *Voyager* spacecraft have to ensure, regardless of cost, that the instrument packages for landing on Mars are thoroughly decontaminated of all terrestrial micro-organisms, so our human operations on Earth must henceforward be undertaken with primary regard to minimizing unthinking interference with the environment. To be able to act in this manner, we have to be rich, and we have to be able to get most of our food without farming. Adoption of the environment game thus goes hand in hand with the synthetic production of food: indeed each is likely to develop only in proportion to the other.

CHAPTER 8

The Environment Game

THE CHIEF consequence of the replacement of much of agriculture by factory production of food would be the liberation of huge areas of the Earth's land surface for other purposes. If one assumes that a quarter of the diet of three times as many people will continue to be produced by agriculture, but perhaps with twice the present average yields per acre, then more than 60 per cent of the present agricultural land will become available for parkland. Of course, a large part of the land now used for livestock is in the form of rough grazing, but even so, great tracts of low-lying land of the first quality would become available for redevelopment. It will then require considerable skill on the part of ecologists to establish balanced, self-controlled flora and fauna in the long-farmed lands, where there may be only archaeological evidence of what the natural cover was before men cleared it, and where climatic changes are known to have occurred since those times. But it can be done, and the result will be a cheerful wilderness where all men can spend a notable fraction of their lives as gamekeepers and hunters.

Moreover, synthetic food production makes more practicable the occupation of any spot on Earth: the mountain ranges, the true deserts, the polar wastes. In these regions, there may be little game to keep, but there will be other rewards of life from the challenging environment. The worst areas may not be worth bothering with, but in many mountainous and arid regions the task of making them habitable for wild life and for men, by raising the tree line or supplying water for example, should be absorbing enough. The oceans afford even huger living space. We can expect to see the development of mid-ocean towns on stable, stationed platforms. From these men will set forth in rubber suits and submersibles to explore the greatest depths and to hunt the big fish.

The total surface area of the planet Earth (land, sea, and ice) is 200 million square miles. If we exclude a quarter of this in particularly unfavoured or protected regions, a world population of 9,000 million could be distributed at a density of sixty per square mile, which is roughly the present population density of the United States.

TOWNS IN THE WILDERNESS

We are now ready to begin the detailed phase of the composition of our possible future, based on the environment game whose principles were stated in the last chapter. The chief practical requirements can be seen to be those of distributing the population much more evenly over land and sea, while confining urban building and other interference with the natural environment to as small an area as may be reasonable, bearing in mind what we shall doubtless understand in greater detail in the foreseeable future—the bad physical and psychological effects of human overcrowding.

It is convenient to think in terms of a town or unit of

population of arbitrary size, although we may expect that towns will always vary greatly in size as at present. To match the population density of 60 per square mile, and figures given elsewhere in the book, I shall choose a unit of 50,000 people commanding an area of 900 square miles of land or sea. It would be equally possible to envisage a group of 500 people with 9 square miles, or a super-city of 50 million people commanding nearly a million square miles—the size of Western Europe.

Food supplies will be produced largely synthetically, although supplemented by gardens, orchards, and green-houses on the one hand, and by hunting for sport on the other. If sunlight is used as the source of energy, collectors of about one square mile will be required on the surface; if nuclear fusion becomes available in small economic units, no surface area will be required and the plant can be put underground or underwater. The gardens might occupy ten square miles on land (one acre per eight people), probably less at sea.

Housing on land can be arranged at will, up to an area of about ten square miles, but it may be hoped that, in accordance with the spirit of the environment game, this area will be kept as small as possible. Indeed, just as the ocean dwellers have to live in ship-like confines, as discussed in a moment, so the concept of a town may be of a ship on land, compact and neat, disturbing the surroundings as little as possible.

In any case, the town will often be enclosed in a dome or some other overall roof, and have its own power supplies and electronic and mechanical workshops. It will also have comprehensive waste-recovery facilities for water, sewage, and discarded manufactured goods, so that the requirements for "imported" raw materials are small.

In this notion of a "closed-cycle eco-system" the architect will draw on experience with spaceships and long-endurance submarines.

The floating town, for that majority of the human race that will eventually settle on the sea, will reach deep underwater so that disturbance due to surface winds and waves will be negligible. Sea-sickness will then be no problem. In metal ships, a concept already exists in the "flip-ship" of the American oceanographers: a long cylinder that can proceed to its station horizontally and then be stood on end by flooding the appropriate spaces.

To provide generous living space at sea would, however, be extremely expensive if provided by conventional shipbuilding means. Passenger ships with their machinery cost something of the order of £1,000 per ton, where one ton represents 100 cu. ft. Even if the self-multiplying wealth of automation enables us to contemplate reasonably expensive items without dismay, this is far too much, and in any case represents a deployment of resources so large that resettlement of a substantial part of the human race on the oceans, with reasonable accommodation, might take hundreds of years. Moreover, conventional seaborne structures have a limited life and would need renewal.

There is, however, a fairly obvious possibility that needs relatively little material input—mainly a supply of energy—and that is the ice ship. Such a possibility was seriously considered during the Second World War for an unsinkable aircraft carrier, code name *Habakkuk*. In the wartime context, even the discovery that wood fibre could greatly toughen the ice was not sufficient to make the project seem feasible. The whole vessel would have had to be kept at −15°C. by an elaborate system of refrigeration pipes, and even then it would have been subject to slow deformation under its own weight. It is, however, entirely plausible that continued study of methods of reinforcement, and an engineering evaluation of an even larger vessel, not required to move and continually regenerated by new ice formation, will lead to the construction of platforms of indefinite life even in warm seas.

Ice has several advantages. Extension and restoration of the platform can be a continuous, automatic process, using refrigeration plant driven by the town's ordinary power supply. Ice is literally unsinkable, and there is a wide margin of safety; even in the event of a power failure, melting would be very slow, as the structure would be encased in an insulating film—of expanded plastic, for example. On the aesthetic side, there is the opportunity for easy landscaping. Building on ice presents special difficulties for the engineer and architect, but probably none of them is insuperable. The inhabitant of such an ice-borne city would be largely unaware of the ice in his daily life; cold would be the least of the problems. It is probable that much of the town would be enclosed by a dome or domes, as protection against wind.

The ocean gardens will perhaps be of three kinds—conventional on imported soil, soil-less cultivation (hydroponics) on the platform, and enclosed and cultivated tanks of sea water.

Within the town, whether on land or sea, the temperature, humidity, and ionic content of the air will be regulated, and this, combined with large-scale roofing and lighting, will maintain spring-like conditions all the year round, or such variations as communities may choose. Perfumes might be used as well as sights and sounds for the embellishment of the environment. Within such areas, buildings will provide multi-storey accommodation and thoroughfares, with sound-proof panelling for privacy; but the chief interest of building will be to create an interesting and ever-changing environment. The same will be true of clothing: it will be ornamental rather than protective.

Transport is perhaps the element most sensitive to the physical size and population of a city. In larger cities, rapid-transit systems in three dimensions will, of course, be essential, but within a town of 50,000 and only a couple of miles in diameter, most personal movements will be on foot or by muscle-powered vehicles like bicycles, with escalators and conveyors (moving footways) helping out. Heavy loads will go by travelling cranes suspended on cables from the roof enclosures. Noise of machinery will be absent.

But what will be counted much more important than transport will be the telecommunications systems linking the inhabitants of the town with one another, with the rest of the world, with computers and with stored information of all kinds—books, music, and visual recordings. Each person will have his own telecommunications set which he can use at will for supervising machinery, for convening a meeting, for calling a relative in another town, for composing music, for learning a language, for playing chess or for almost any purpose that does not require physical contact with people or objects—in addition, of course, to entertainment and news broadcasts of conventional kinds. A man will be able to wander freely through the world without leaving his town—making chance contacts with other wanderers, perhaps "sharing" a meal with a stranger on the other side of the world, or consulting a professor in a distant university.

Ample communications channels provided by radio or optical means, via communications satellites, will be the key to such systems, but computers will also play a crucial part, with one or more installations in each town shared by the inhabitants and linked in a world-wide network. The only limits to the uses of the system will be those of privacy. Not only will each user be able at any time to exclude interruption by callers, and to conduct business in complete secrecy, he will also be protected, at least if the democratic ideal persists, against supervision or interference by authority. The computer need not be Big Brother. On the other hand, even though motives for felonies will no doubt still exist, their execution will be made virtually impossible in most cases by automatic alarms and similar devices, including personal distress transmitters.

A central feature of life within the town will be the facilities for continuous observation of the surrounding land or ocean. These will be the link between the town and what will be the chief practical preoccupation of its inhabitants—the care of the wilderness outside. In the case of a land area, cameras working by light and by infra-red rays (to show animal movements in the dark), sensitive microphones, and instruments recording physical and chemical changes in the environment, will be disposed unobtrusively throughout the area, so that anyone at any time can observe the natural life at any spot in great detail, without intruding into it. A child will grow up with intimate knowledge of the wild life around him, and some of the birds and larger mammals at least he will recognize as individuals.

In the case of a sea area, there will be important differences in the instrumentation, and the volume observed will be much greater, but the principles will be much the same. This instrumentation will be primarily scientific and educational in purpose, but it will also enable both routine inspection (for conservation purposes) and the individual's general view of the area to be maintained continuously. It will be a supplement to, not a substitute for, direct personal experience of the environment.

Life outside the town will be altogether different. The air-conditioned, computer-served artificial environment will be exchanged for an altogether more "natural" one. To be sure, there will be the little concealed instruments; and by careful manipulation in planting, stocking, and culling of the plant, animals, and micro-organisms, the environment will be kept under extensive human control. But the aim of such activities will be to maximize the diversity and natural productivity of the area, so that the overriding "rules" will not be man-made, and the area, superficially at least, will be indistinguishable from virgin territory. All direct evidence of past human activity— roads, houses, farms, plantations—excepting only the recent footfall and man's ancient and more precious monuments will be gone. Even if the inhabitants of the town spend on average half their lives in the countryside or the water, they can spread themselves very thinly.

There is a useful conception here from the theory of gases, with a suitably evocative name: the "mean free path". The mean free path is the mean distance a molecule travels without colliding with another one. This, translated into movements of people at random upon a two-dimensional surface, gives us an idea of how free a man may feel in the wilderness, in contrast with the confines of the town and the potential immediate communication with the rest of the human world that he has there.

At a density at any one time of thirty people per square mile or, say, ten groups or individuals per square mile, that allows an average separation of a third of a mile between groups. One will pass within fifty yards of another only about once every mile and a half of travel— or, say, once an hour, while a man could travel for thirty miles and only speak to two other groups (assuming a "speaking distance" of five yards). In most fertile territory, moreover, groups will be concealed from one another for much of the time by vegetation and rising ground. At sea the opacity of the water and the greater opportunity for movement in the third dimension will provide even greater isolation.

When a man walks out through the gates of his town, he will leave civilization behind except, if he chooses, for a radio link with the town and with other men in the wilderness. The landsman, however, like the sea-dweller, will be encased in technologically developed clothes, which will enable him to withstand heat or cold, or rain or wind indefinitely without having to retreat to shelter: he will be able to lie down and sleep anywhere. He will not even need to make a fire when he stops for the night, unless he does so for his own pleasure. There will be a few recognized sleeping grounds where people can meet. Here, food supplies and water will be available from underground caches, but there will be no structures.

HUNTERS AND GAMEKEEPERS

What will everyone *do* in the wilderness? There are two main answers: one is to hunt; the other is to conserve.

The only rational and humane rate of hunting for a

group of people is that which will provide their food for the period allocated to them for hunting. The population density will be such that, allowing for sound conservation of the hunted species, each person might live for the equivalent of about one year of his life on game. But each hunter may be willing to take three or four unarmed helpers with him in addition to his family; so that, as boy and man, if the women tend to opt out, an individual could spend the equivalent of four or five years of his life as a serious hunter, or a month a year. Moreover, the eyes and skills of the hunter can be cultivated all his life, in his knowledge of the spoor and the ways of the wild. Mock hunting can be effectively contrived by the use of guns loaded with cine-film which register the aim when the trigger is pulled.

Augmenting the difficulties of the serious hunter's task, which might otherwise be too easy in view of his lifelong scientific knowledge of the territory, will be the fact that his licence will stipulate the individual, separately identified mammals and birds that he may take. This will ensure that the culling is in precise accord with conservation plans. As for the weapons, modern crossbows are finding favour among game authorities nowadays; if guns were used, they would have to be silenced.

Indeed, it will be very important to minimize disturbance of any kind, because the presence of so many human beings moving about in the wilderness could reduce the animals to a state of perpetual agitation. This requirement sets limits on human conduct and technology. Everyone, hunter or not, will move with stealth, and will pride himself on the unconcern of the animals around him. Aircraft and other vehicles must be almost silent, including those for long-distance travel between towns, which have to pass over the wilderness. For this reason, if for no other, I expect that there will be a revival of airships as a primary form of transport, both for use within the wilderness and also on longer journeys for reaching rocket stations if near-orbital speeds are really required. For most people, with time to spare, non-stop travel by nuclear-powered airship at, say, 400 miles an hour will be fast enough, taking them to the Antipodes in less than a day and a half and enabling them to observe the wilderness on the way.

I have already mentioned, directly or by implication, several elements and constraints of the conservation programme: the eradication of human structures; the concealed instrumentation of the wilderness; the culling role of the hunter; the need for stealth. It will be clear that, in the methods as well as in the scale of the operations, the scheme envisages something altogether more ambitious than present limited attempts at conservation.

Some explanation is, perhaps, needed about the aims of conservation. Its purpose is not to preserve museums of wild life. Some direct action will doubtless be needed, as at present, to maintain examples of disappearing species in special reserves or zoos. Nor is the objective to produce pretty countryside or maintain an agreeable playground for human beings—although these secondary requirements will be taken into account and often the conservation programme will succeed admirably in both respects. Within the rules of the environment game, the primary aim is to sustain diverse and active living communities, in which non-human life can resume in comparative tranquillity the ponderous process of evolution which has been so disrupted and confused by the irruption of man. But man can lend a helping hand.

"Biotechnology", the application of the life sciences, may take many strange and wonderful forms within the laboratories and factories of the cities, but in the wilderness it will be altogether more discreet. Every factor influencing the environment will be closely studied; every species and its variations will be known intimately. The complex interactions between species will be followed day by day and year by year.

In the oceans, especially, a great deal of effort to begin with will be required simply to learn about the environment. But on land, much of the environment has been irretrievably altered from its "natural" state by the activities of men and of their animals and plants. In such areas, when the demolition of man-made structures has been done, there will be immense scope for human inventiveness and experiment in re-establishing wild ecological systems. What combinations of species, indigenous and exotic, will establish a viable, fruitful, and plastic system, in which the characteristics of each species will operate to best effect? Can selection or modification of varieties enable the species to flourish even better?

Co-ordination of conservation policies between adjacent regions will be essential, if intruding species from one area are not to play havoc in another, as happened with the introduction of the rabbit in Australia. Established migration routes of birds, mammals, and fishes have to be respected. On the other hand, acceptable differences in ecological approach in nearby areas will be a useful corrective to excessive planning by men, and will give species a chance to extend their range.

Plainly, the relationship between men and the wilderness will be a delicate one. Since the invention of agriculture, it has not been possible to leave the wild species on land to look after themselves. But in future men will have to make decisions determining in large measure the fate of species. There is every reason why this should be done with great humility; for all our growing knowledge of physiology and genetics, and our new techniques for administering complex systems, our knowledge and imagination will still be unable fully to grasp the evolutionary potential of all species, from elephants to viruses. For planning purposes, men will have to draw up tentative models of how a given ecological system will develop; but, if they are wrong, and when, as is bound to happen, a certain species does better or worse than expected, the last thing they should do is to force the system to conform to their models, with guns or chemicals. Instead, they should allow the system to change, while fostering or introducing other, controlling species that may help to prevent too violent an excursion from the overall balance.

From the viewpoint of the environment game, man the hunter is the one species in the system under almost complete control, and because of his versatility and power as a predator, he can select any species for attack. The conservationist can readily compute, at any season, what population of hunters the system can support. As has been suggested, he will identify the individual animals that the hunters can take. But he must again resist the temptation to use the hunters to rectify "mistakes" in his planning: the quotas of species for hunting must be to a certain extent randomized within minimum and maximum limits. In short, the conservationist is not God.

On the contrary, conservation policy will be a matter of sharp and continuous controversy, and properly so because the dilemma of planning versus anarchy in the wilderness is not likely ever to be susceptible to objective resolution. It will be the chief concern of practical politics, at least at the local level.

Just as we have estimated the scope for hunting, so we must now assess how much human time can usefully and interestingly be spent in other ways in the wilderness. We can distinguish at least four activities and, for purposes of calculation, guess at the number of men who could constructively be engaged in them at any one time. In practice, specialization will be avoided and each person can take part in most if not all of the activities. The danger, of course, is that excessive zeal or officiousness in conservation will lead to unnecessary small-scale interference with the environment—endless "tidying up" which begins to be reminiscent of the farmer with his hoe. The numbers given here will, I believe, be small enough; they apply to our arbitrary area of 900 square miles (total human population, 50,000). The explanations of the different functions are given in relation to land-dwelling; with little modification they can be applied equally to the oceans.

(1) *Environmental research* (3,000 men)

Study in detail of all the ecological systems of the wilderness: food chains and interactions of species, soil fertility, population fluctuations, animal behaviour, diseases, and the influence of physical conditions on biological productivity.

Anatomy, physiology, and genetics of all local species.

Local geology, hydrology, and meteorology.

Upper atmosphere research and observation of the Sun's activities.

Instrumentation of the wilderness for general as well as scientific purposes.

(2) *Model-making* (1,000 men)

Comparative studies of the ecology of other localities.

Theoretical analysis of ecological and genetic consequences of modifications to biological systems.

Construction and testing of computer models of the future of the total environment on various assumptions, as a guidance to management.

(3) *Management and control* (4,000 men)

Decisions on broad policies of human interference with the wilderness, including introduction, eradication or modification of species, landscaping, modification of water supplies, special temporary use of fertilizers, etc.

Ad hoc decisions on small-scale modifications, such as clearance of ponds or treatment of a plant or animal disease.

Implementation of decisions, excluding the killing of the largish mammals and birds reserved for the hunters.

Designation of individual animals for hunting, in accordance with conservation policy.

Control and licensing of all human activities in the wilderness.

Judging human performance, e.g., in hunting, for purposes of prizes and rewards.

Miscellaneous activities such as fire-fighting, rescue of humans and animals in distress, and maintenance of food and water caches.

(4) *Intelligence* (4,000 men)

Systematic patrol and observation in detail of day-by-day and season-by-season changes in the wilderness, in support of research and management and as a continuous check on the outcome of policies. It is through this activity that men become intimately familiar with their environment.

To satisfy himself that these are not over-generous figures, the reader may like to note that in each category the numbers engaged are fewer than five per square mile. In each square mile of fertile country there will typically be thousands of trees, birds and fish, hundreds of mammals, many millions of insects, and microbes beyond number. Every species is of consuming interest in understanding the environment.

If we add to these figures 4,000 for the number of men engaged as hunters or hunters' helpers at any one time, we have a total of 16,000, which is roughly equal to the number of males in the local population aged over twenty-two. We have not yet taken account of any of the conventional activities within the town, including the supervision of manufacturing processes, retailing, teaching, administration, non-environmental research, health services, housekeeping, and care of the very young and very old. Moreover, contributions to "big science" projects such as space exploration will occupy some of the people, and with study, arts, entertainment, and sports *ad lib.*, no one need feel he has time on his hands, and those women who choose to take an active part in the game can readily be accommodated.

It may be objected that not many men nowadays are "naturalists" and are unlikely to take kindly to the role of scientific gamekeeper. My own belief is that, having regard to our Palaeolithic ancestry, the great majority would much prefer it to, say, being a clerk or a machine-minder. And for the minority who do not want to step outside the town, there is plenty for them to do inside—for example, in the instrumentation laboratory or the records office—which enables them still to participate in the environment game even if botany bores them stiff.

And, as we have said, anyone who is simply not prepared to play the game can continue to live in reasonable comfort, even though he cannot expect to "succeed" socially—unless it is as one of the small band of professional sportsmen or artists.

There are so many ways of apportioning responsibilities and rewards in the environment game, and developing career patterns, that a period of experiment will probably be necessary before a favoured social structure emerges. Drawing the analogy from the hunting-bands and clans of our forefathers, one possibility is lifelong membership by each person of a particular squad, which engages as a unit in most of the activities mentioned. A man may, by reason of his interests or responsibilities, be semipermanently detached from the squad, but his social affiliation to it will remain and his wife and children will continue as honorary members of the squad.

GLOBAL INTERESTS

The set-up described, with ship-like communities in the wilderness and comprehensive global communications, will tend to polarize human interests to the town and the world. With near self-sufficiency of the towns in food and raw materials, the nation-state may tend to wither, for technological rather than doctrinaire reasons. The "big science" projects like space exploration will be thoroughly internationalized, and it is entirely reasonable to envisage these being supported by contributions in kind from the towns.

The survival of the nation-state as a recognizable entity will be assured for many years for geographical, geological, and linguistic reasons. Certain operations, notably higher education, mining, heavy engineering, and transport, are most naturally organized on a regional basis, and if there are disputes between towns these, too, can logically remain the concern of a national system of justice. The residue of political dogma will give plenty of motive for trying to preserve large geographical areas from opposing creeds, and allowance must be made for the lust for imperial power that consumes many men.

If there is one respect in which radical changes of ideas are bound to occur, however, that is in defence. The deployment of nuclear weapons and other systems of great power may be, however regrettably, the chief mark of national authority. But from a more practical military point of view, the existence in each locality of large numbers of highly trained scientists-*cum*-hunters—skilled in arms and electronics and knowing the country more intimately than anyone has ever done before—will provide a built-in defence against would-be invaders. It will become nearly impossible for outsiders to effect conventional military or naval occupation. While the towns will remain vulnerable to nuclear attack, quite simple systems of defensive missiles can make any attempt to seize the towns with, say, airborne troops, far too costly to contemplate. The very self-confidence that this situation engenders will help to diminish the fears on which arms races and wars are built.

There is a paradox in the matter of trade in goods: it is held nowadays to be one of the chief bonds between nations yet, as it diminishes when each region and town becomes more self-sufficient, that trend may make co-operation between men easier. International trade reinforces the importance of a nation and, at the present time, the need to maintain national balances of payments in the face of fierce trading competition is making technology extremely nationalistic in its orientation.

World government constituted as a matter of principle seems a very remote ideal, granting the depth of divisions between different groups since Palaeolithic times. The growth of global institutions, on the other hand, will create a *de facto* world government covering a large part of human activity. It will come about in spite of, rather than because of, political aspirations and, far from being based on ideals of brotherhood, it will be forced on mankind by the need to control and co-ordinate a proliferation of *ad hoc* operations. These will include:

"Big science" projects.

Supra-national engineering and development enterprises.

Global telecommunications and transport.

Health services, especially in respect of communicable diseases.

Internationalized universities.

Meteorological services and climate-control experiments.

Colonization of the oceans.

In budgetary terms, as the turnover of these institutions will grow out of proportion to that of purely national enterprises, the national government will become a mere post office between its own citizens and the world authorities.

This is not at all a fanciful idea: it exists in embryonic form in the specialized agencies of the United Nations (International Telecommunication Union, World Health Organization, UNESCO, etc.), in collaborative scientific and technological enterprises for space research, high-energy physics, molecular biology, supersonic airliners and so on, in great international businesses like Shell and IBM, and in miscellaneous outfits such as Interpol (criminal investigation), Eurovision (TV programme exchange) and locust-control agencies.

CIVILIZED LIFE

In consolidating some of the general features of life under the environment game, we should note that differences in detail of social organization (possibly deriving from tradition or political dogma) are far less important than the establishment of the new social objectives and the ecological and technological features that match them. With a large number of smallish communities, in diverse environments, there will be endless opportunity for social experiment. Nevertheless some principles can be suggested.

There should be a suitable balance between complete freedom for the individual to do as he pleases on the one hand and clear indications of what he should do to play the environment game in concert with his fellows and to be "successful". This is probably a threefold matter of (1) fixing minimal living standards regardless of a man's contribution, (2) devising a fair system of promotion and rewards within the area of direct conservation and related activities and (3) retaining something of the present money/power system to cover activities that do not fit into the main local system.

Education need no longer be a formal activity. Just as the nature of the environment game tends to eradicate the conventional distinction between work and leisure, so one may set about getting rid of the tradition that education is something that takes place in classes at set hours. The distinction between learning and living can disappear once it is accepted that acquiring knowledge and skills is not a socially necessary preamble to real life but the real stuff of human existence. Even the segregation into teachers and pupils can become obsolescent.

The great technological revolution in education will come from the computer-communications network and from the possibility of securing at any time or place not just information but a lecture or a programmed teaching course in any subject. This access to knowledge, and the handling by information storage of all that is routine to education means that the function of the teacher is much more interesting and constructive. He has to guide the dupil through the storehouse of knowledge and engenper the will to learn in a disciplined fashion. But as the teacher may have little knowledge of some of the subjects pursued by his pupil, he too will be learning all the time; moreover, within the environment game, the eyes of the child or young person looking at his environment may have special insights denied to more sophisticated men and so the teacher may dispose himself to learn from his pupil. In the new concept, much teaching can be done by people not specially designated as teachers.

But in any case most learning will be by doing, throughout life. Learning the environment game can begin in earnest as soon as the child is old enough to step out into the wilderness and mimic the hunters; elementary knowledge of all the environmental arts and sciences will come as a matter of course. For other subjects, the student of languages will travel; the student of history will consult original sources at the flick of a switch; science and engineering will be mastered in real experiments and constructions. Mathematics and an understanding of complex systems will be acquired through familiarity from childhood with the computer and the patterns it generates. The written examination will disappear, but "paper qualifications" may still be awarded on the basis of dissertations and practical tests.

Each town will be its own university, but people of all ages will travel to other towns to broaden their outlook and to master particular subjects with the appropriate authorities, because centres of excellence will naturally establish themselves for specialized scholarship and research. Here, as with exchanges by telecommunications, there may be little need for accountancy; the student will benefit the town he visits while he is there.

To visualize the educational potential of the town of 50,000, we may suppose that, using present-day degrees as an index, half the population will proceed to something equivalent to a pass or honours degree in their youth, quite a few more will "graduate" later in life, and about 10 per cent will be capable of higher degrees. Thus one may envisage an "undergraduate" population of about 1,500 and about 200 "postgraduate" students. But these artificial categories will scarcely exist; everyone will be learning, practising, experimenting, and from time to time individuals will be deemed ready to advance into more exacting activities. People will be judged not by what brains or knowledge they have, but by what use they make of it.

For "big science" projects, and for large-scale mining and heavy industrial undertakings, the towns will provide not only material contributions but manpower as well. Men will therefore leave their towns for a period, as volunteers, to exercise their special skills or just for the sake of sampling a different environment.

In sum, the basis of the local and global economies will be the informed mind, its voluntary application to interesting tasks and its ability to multiply material and non-material wealth up to the limits of the environment and the human nervous system. Wherever a man and his mind goes, whatever he does within the framework of the environment game, he is of ample service to the local community to merit its support for himself and his family. The requirement for special status, honours, and rewards only arises for reasons of administration, incentive, and the common wish to give recognition to achievement.

We may suppose, for the sake of example, that the value-system of a typical community may rate success in the game as depending in comparable measure on the following qualities:

Skill and endurance as hunter/gamekeeper

Creative ability in science, technology, and the arts

General qualities of courage, gentleness, truthfulness, etc.

While the first two are echoes of the military and intellectual roads to power, entrepreneurial or administrative skill is omitted because the computer makes it commonplace; and so, too, is "leadership". The latter omission is plausible because qualities of leadership will be manifest primarily in the new free-for-all educational process, so that the "born leader" acts directly and continuously on the minds of his fellow men. His influence permeates his community and its programmes without him having to secure power. In primitive democracies of the present day we believe we need leaders on the top of the heap, as it were, although it is really a negation of the democratic principle. In a self-sufficient, self-confident, highly educated democracy, all one wants are chairmen.

Thus political or administrative responsibility may become a relatively minor prize in the game, at least in the example here given. Esteem, special accommodation and facilities, special hunting rights and so on, go to the brilliant hunter, the inspired artist, the ingenious mathematician, the brave firefighter and so on; given a clear and broad set of values, it will usually be obvious who has done well, and most honest men in the course of their lives will achieve distinction and special reward of some kind or other. Gross violation of these standards is another matter.

This brings us to crime, and here the situation can be expected to change remarkably. In the context of the environment game, next only to murder, vandalism is the worst crime; and all real crimes can be seen as vandalism. Wilful damage to the town's equipment, making a nerve-racking noise, unauthorized destruction of living things in the wilderness, treasonable action with an external enemy—all these tend to frustrate the community's purpose of maintaining the environment. Deceit or crimes of violence rank equally as vandalism against the human mind and body. As crimes of violence can probably be effectively deterred by the use of personal distress transmitters, untruthfulness or bad faith will come to be taken much more seriously than they are today. Theft will be largely obsolete, because with computerized accounting it will be largely impracticable and immediately discoverable. But the most effective deterrent to crime will be the way of dealing with it: the force of social disapproval in a closely knit community and, in extreme cases, denial of rights or expulsion. There will be no jails, because the community will not be in the least frightened of the offenders.

Turning to other aspects of life within the town, there will be opportunity to make sure that the human engineering principle—the matching of the constructed environment to the man rather than vice versa—is allowed to operate right down to the level of individual choice. In other words, food, clothes, furniture, electronic consoles, etc., should be susceptible to individual taste in much greater detail than that provided by the choice of mass-produced goods in present-day shops. This means that the machinery producing them will have to be much more flexible than a conventional production line. But with computer-controlled food blenders, knitting machines, machine tools, and circuit printers it will be easy to arrange. Indeed, this is one of the ways in which distinguishable "work" will vanish for, given communal workshops, each person will simply go along when he needs, say, a chair or a suit, and either sketch one for himself or select drawings by a skilled designer; the machinery will then produce it in a few moments. Only the raw materials need be rationed, by financial or other means.

Similarly, each home will be an experimental eco-system, in which the individual will contrive to maintain an agreeable material life for his family with the minimum use of external resources or physical interference with the neighbours. Small children will acquire a general appreciation of the environment game, even before they see it applied in detail in the wilderness. The spirit is that of "do-it-yourself", because doing is learning; but the tools can be the most sophisticated that technology has to offer. Just as the distinction between research and "real life" will disappear, so will the segregation of the arts. There will be no dividing line between the housewife programming a computer to weave her a tablecloth and the sculptor making a monument for a public garden—only gradations of talent.

We can now tidy up a few further ends of applied science, by noting some basic requirements, some contributory aids to the environment game and some technologies that are positively disfavoured.

Energy—several kilowatts per head—will come primarily from nuclear fusion or sunlight if feasible, otherwise from nuclear fission. Fluid fuels, like petrol, paraffin and gas, will continue to be tapped from underground deposits or manufactured as required, because of their convenience for many purposes, especially in conjunction with fuel cells as a "private" source of electricity.

Transport, as I have said, will be mainly by silent airships and submersibles, and by rockets from launching grounds in desert regions. Noisy vehicles, including aeroplanes, will no longer exist. There will be many satellites in the sky, for communications, for navigation, and for continuous observation of the global environment.

But we should add another technology. To "amplify" a man so that he is capable of uprooting a tree or striding at high speed across difficult country is a possibility already under serious study in the United States. The idea is to give him a suit which is in fact a metal skeleton with powered joints in place of muscle; it responds to natural movements of the arms and legs but with much greater force. It is of particular interest for the wilderness, in the absence of tracks and heavy equipment, although it would be used only for rescue and for special landscape engineering, including demolition of pre-existing man-made structures.

Instrument technology, for surveillance of the wilderness, will be a major activity, with great emphasis on miniaturization and camouflage.

The quest for material self-sufficiency and decentralization of activity envisaged in the network of small towns will emphasize technologies such as the extraction of minerals from water (which would fit in very well with extraction of heavy hydrogen for fusion power) and the development of structural materials from whatever is to hand—mimicking in this respect the ability of living species to make bone, teeth, skin and fibres from very common elements. Mining and heavy engineering will tend to diminish in importance, although local quarrying will continue, integrated with landscaping plans.

As medicine will be largely a matter of automatic bio-chemical tests, computer diagnosis and treatment by obvious drugs, and as nearly everyone will be both healthy and well versed in human pathology, there will be little need for doctors except in the sense of personal care, teaching, and research, which will devolve naturally enough on fellow-citizens. Surgery will almost disappear, except for treatment of accidents and replacement of diseased or damaged parts, and the latter will probably be done only in centres of excellence.

To elaborate further on social and technological aspects of the environment game would be to narrow its apparent scope. If the general framework can be established, matching human virtues and vices, the details can be varied at will without frustrating the main purposes.

But how do we get from here to there? Clarifying the necessary steps is the last task but one for the composer.

IS IT POSSIBLE?

Superficially, the transition appears hopeless, in the face of desperate efforts to expand agriculture, the growth of megalopolis, the intensification of nationalistic rivalries in political, military, and economic fields, and the ruthless economic tests that govern human activities even in wealthy countries. But in fact there are very strong grounds for optimism.

They lie chiefly in technology. Our institutions are shaped by our economic game, which in turn is moulded by our choice of technologies—at the base by agriculture as the principal way of obtaining food, but with all the paraphernalia of modern civilization superimposed to force the individual into sustaining the game as the productivity of agriculture goes up. Politicians have, however, scarcely grasped the fact that innovations such as the motor car, penicillin, or computers have a far more profound effect on how people live than do their minor tinkerings with the rules of the game.

It is my belief that, by selecting the right technologies for special development (by the authority of relatively casual political decisions), we can create a revolutionary situation in which the adoption of the environment game, or something like it, will be virtually inevitable.

These technologies, in summary, in rough order of importance and with an evaluation of present efforts, are:

Birth control (inadequate)
Synthesis of food (slight)
Automation to multiply wealth and create apparent
    redundancy (good)

Biotechnology of conservation, land and sea (inadequate)

Enclosure of towns to discourage urban sprawl (slight)

Ice engineering, to lead to ocean platforms (inadequate)

Application of complex-system analysis to human affairs (inadequate)

Technologies of decentralization:

Computer-communications networks (good)

Self-sufficiency in energy and raw materials (inadequate)

Small-scale, versatile manufacturing techniques (inadequate)

Close-cycle human eco-systems (good, e.g. space ships)

Applied psychology of human communal life (inadequate)

There are other developments, such as space technology and undersea technology, which are broadly in harmony with the ambitions for the environment game; some (dam-building and forestry, for example) which are more or less neutral, and some, particularly motorways, noisy aircraft, electricity grids, huge factories and offices, which are inimical to the long-term objective. As observed earlier (Chapter 3), the necessary enlargement of agriculture to feed the rising population, until synthetic food begins to take effect, should be done as far as possible within existing cultivated areas.

One of the necessary technologies which is already in full swing is automation. While it does not itself suggest the environment game it will play the key negative role of turning the present-day game into a farce. By about the end of this century there will be an embarrassment of material riches in many countries. The computer-communications network will be substantially complete. By then, too, large-scale synthetic food production will have begun and, given sufficient effort, should be reaching the point at which agricultural production no longer needs to grow to keep abreast of population; the subsequent decline of agriculture will, however, be relatively slow, so that it may not be until well into the twenty-first century that the large tracts of farmland have been released for restoration of the wilderness.

Nevertheless, by the start of the new century the time will be ripe to swap games. Because of the emphasis on self-sufficiency within each community, with a view to minimizing its effects on the environment, it will be entirely possible for the old and the new games to coexist for a while, in different nations and even within a single nation. In the latter case, it is simply a matter of arbitrarily allocating substantial resources to environmental development, out of the public revenues as measured by the rules of the present-day game—just as wealth is currently set aside for defence, education, research, and space exploration.

If the aim is to redistribute the human species more evenly over the Earth's surface, large-scale migration is inevitable, and all sorts of awkward political questions arise. The basic pattern would have to be that, from countries where the population density is much more than sixty per square mile, people would move either into countries of much lower population density or into the oceans. The growth of populations in the meantime will mean that current figures are not a good guide, but there are some obvious areas of overpopulation (notably Europe, South-East Asia, the Caribbean) and some obvious wide-open spaces on land (notably Australia, Siberia, Canada, and much of South America). The political barriers to migration (racial prejudice or fear of take-over, for example) will be reinforced by economic questions of who is to pay the considerable capital costs of resettlement. In any case, some countries—probably the richer ones—will adopt the environment game earlier than others.

A plausible sequence is the following:

(1) Re-settlement with more even distribution of population *within* the USSR and North America;

(2) Migration of Japanese into the Pacific and of Europeans into the Atlantic, Mediterranean and Baltic;

(3) Re-settlement within the African continent and Indonesia, Malaysia, and Indo-China;

(4) Migration from the Caribbean and the American isthmus into South America;

(5) Migration of Indians and Pakistanis into the Indian Ocean;

(6) Migration of the Chinese into the Pacific and, subject to political considerations, into Siberia.

In this sequence, even if the details are wrong, we can see some important features. The greatest opportunity for establishing the principles of the environment game exists in the USSR and North America. Secondly, the responsibility for pioneering the colonization of the oceans probably rests on the Europeans and Japanese and matches well their maritime traditions. (In Europe, the most densely populated large nations are England, Holland, Belgium, Germany, and Italy.) Thirdly, what is politically most significant by present standards is the eventual spread of the Chinese northwards and far into the Pacific.

A singular opportunity arises with the colonization of the oceans, but unfortunately there is no certainty that it will be properly seized. It arises from the historical acceptance of the idea that the oceans belong to no one—the "freedom of the seas". If the oceans are to be parcelled out to colonists, therefore, it follows that only a supra-national authority could legitimately do so. Two consequences are (1) that such an authority (at present, the United Nations) could charge royalties or rents for the use of ocean space and resources, thereby acquiring far greater revenues than it does today, for its general work; and (2) that it can allocate space in such a way as to create extra-national "states" of any desired composition and constitution owing allegiance to the global authority. By such a process, world government can grow in an *ad hoc* way, without offering any direct challenge to the political independence of the nations, until the day comes when roughly half of the human species is so organized, in its ocean towns.

There are plenty of ways in which such an outcome can be frustrated: by the need to finance settlement on a national basis; by powerful nations laying claim, by force of arms, to large areas of ocean; by discord within the ocean "state"; by belligerent attitudes between the watermen and landsmen; and so on. The existence of exploitable mineral and biological resources in the ocean will encourage land nations to seek rights in the oceans. If the opportunity is missed in the next few years to legislate for the international development of the oceans, the commitment of national interest and resources may become so great that *de facto* "nationalization" of tracts of ocean may be impossible to reverse without conflict.

We must also ask how quickly the necessary resettlement

can be accomplished. To obtain a rough impression of the answer it is convenient to make a nationalistic calculation. Consider the British Isles, comprising relatively wealthy countries, but ones which will have to spread a very large part of their population into the oceans—a more expensive operation than spreading on land (as the Russians, for example, can do).

If the population of the British Isles at the end of the century is about eighty million, and if the population density for the environment game is to be sixty per square mile, more than 90 per cent of the British, and 50 per cent of the Southern Irish, are candidates for resettlement in the surrounding waters. This means the construction of, say, 1,400 ocean-platforms for 50,000 people each. The capital cost of each, including synthetic-food plant and all facilities, may be cautiously estimated at £500 million (1966 prices), but this is not all extra cost as part of it could be incurred anyway in housing and services on land. By the end of the century, the national income of the United Kingdom and Ireland may be £60,000 million (1966 prices), roughly equivalent to the present income per head in the United States. If it then continues to redouble every twenty years, but most of the additional wealth thereafter is used for "tooling up" for the environment game, the construction of the 1,400 ocean towns need take no more than thirty or forty years. There will, of course, be parallel work of resettlement on land, particularly in the Scottish highlands, while demolition of many of the ugly industrial towns of Britain will prepare for the subsequent cut-off of growth of national income and full adoption of the environment game. It may be expected, however, that the British land-dwellers will want to preserve the best of their existing cities, and may for this reason opt for larger urban units than those on the sea.

Thus ashore in England, in seventy years' time, one might find a mere three million people, faced with the big task of recreating the woodland that existed in pre-Neolithic times, living perhaps only in the former cores of a dozen cities, each commanding an area larger than Yorkshire.

Action far less drastic than the British putting most of the population to sea would be required for preparation for the environment game in the United States. There the mean population density is already about right, and remains so for many of the states of the Union. Net movements from the densely populated states of the eastern seaboard and the Great Lakes into the mountain and desert states would be called for.

Whatever may be the detailed obstacles on the way to the establishment of the environment game, and the radical readjustments of human attitudes that may be necessary, we can draw confidence from one scarcely questionable conclusion: that if either the Americans or the Russians chose to adopt the game, they could be fully deployed and equipped for it by the beginning of the twenty-first century. For the rest of us it may take a little longer; but we need not be impatient if we have at last identified a purpose for our technologies and our wealth.

The final task is to check the possible long-term effects of the environment game, over the centuries, such as those which stemmed from agriculture. And here the composer should remember the words of Mr Scandal to Mr Foresight in Congreve's *Love for Love*: "You are a wise man, and a conscientious man; a searcher into obscurity and futurity; and if you commit an error, it is with a great deal of consideration, and discretion, and caution."

Certainly, that remark can be applied to many men through the ages, up to the present day. Mr Foresight put his trust in astrology and physiognomy, which he studied diligently; much of what passes for serious thought today exercises ideas which, while inherently less foolish, may completely miss the important point. In striving to harmonize the interests of men with their technologies and their environment, are we overlooking something crucial?

It may be that the basis of the environment game will be shaken by endless increase in populations. I believe, on the contrary, that the environment game will be a powerful restraint on population growth, because the intimate knowledge of ecology will provide the rational basis for limiting the size of families. But I may be wrong, and the evidence of synthetic food production and wide open spaces could encourage everyone to breed until the world's surface is entirely covered with artificial photosynthesizers. Who can tell?

Again, I have said little about religion, while some contend that a religious or at least a "moral" revival is what men need most. I am wholly sceptical about the ability of any religion, old or new, to guide us through the inevitable technical and social revolutions of the next fifty years. The environment game itself neither encourages nor discourages religion as such, but it may make the classical agrarian religions obsolescent.

A further risk will be that the environment game may, like the present-day game, produce its own crop of cruelties and obsessions, frustrations and conflicts. That is likely, indeed, but the important question is whether the game will tend to amplify or dampen them. In the present-day game it is possible to dress up any madness in terms of "national destiny" or "economic necessity" or "force of circumstance". When the apparatus of the agrarian or industrial nation state is literally bulldozed into oblivion, "economic problems" will be the last thing likely to bother the self-sufficient, automated community, in which everyone can afford to be calmly self-confident and tolerant of waywardness.

What happens afterwards? I doubt if the environment game, as here outlined, could be sufficiently absorbing for more than a few centuries, to remain indefinitely the dominant theme of life. Human ideas will continue to grow and change at high speed. The *reductio ad absurdum* of the environment game would be to vacate Earth, in order to allow the reinvigorated wilderness to find its own evolutionary destiny—to allow, perhaps, a new intelligent species to emerge in our place. Men would then start afresh on another planet. But we can dismiss this kind of possibility: we are of the Earth and this is the home for which we have evolved.

What is more likely is that new interests, that we cannot yet guess at, will seize the energies and minds of men. Then they may be content to leave the wilderness again to the care of a few specialists.

There is a great deal of superstitious talk about the "destiny" of man. Also, among some scientists, there is highly dangerous speculation about "eugenics", the selection for special breeding of desirable human qualities—carrying the implication that men already have more than an inkling of what they are and what they may become. Yet the discoveries of the past 300 years—and especially of the last thirty—in giving us astonishing powers have served to show how squalid are our old-fashioned motives and ambitions. Who are we, who do not understand the nettle or the rabbit, to guess what *men* may be?

To our grandchildren and their children our own struggles and anxieties will seem like the bad dream of an illiterate mind. At present we know just enough to wake with a start, to a fleeting glimpse of what the planet was once like. We can redirect our attention, and that of our own children, to the living environment; also to human skills and insights that were ancient when the mammoth still walked. We can rediscover a forgotten part of ourselves. In laying to rest the ghosts of the other men who stooped to conquer it, we can restore to its proper condition what is still the kindliest place we know—the Blue Planet.

APPENDIX

The Energy Barrier

FOOD IS energy in chemical form, derived from other forms of energy. The supreme merit of agriculture, seen as an industrial process, is that its original source of energy is free. Sunlight is diffuse energy and agriculture makes very inefficient use of it, so that huge areas of land are required for its collection. Nevertheless, in aggregate, the net energy content of human food is substantial and if we were to seek to provide it using original sources of energy other than sunlight the demand would be very great. If, on the other hand, we want to continue to use sunlight, but with much smaller areas, we have to find new methods of energy conversion.

This Appendix to Chapter 6 therefore probes in some numerical and technical detail the "energy barrier" to synthetic food production.

To begin with some simple arithmetic, we can assume the following figures:

World population in AD 2050: 9,000 million (roughly three times the present population)

Net food requirements per head: 3,000 Calories per day

Gross requirements of primary food per head: 5,000 Calories per day (allowing for one-sixth of the diet to be in the form of animal products, converted by real animals from primary food at 20 per cent efficiency)

Efficiency of energy conversion in primary food synthesis: 5 per cent (this is a very rough assumption, implying that, whatever original source of energy is employed, one-twentieth part of it will find its way into the primary food product)

It then follows that the original energy input for our synthetic food production is:

Per head: 100,000 Calories per day

For 9,000 million population: 900 million million Calories per day.

For comparison, the total energy of sunlight falling on the world's cultivated land at present is about fifty times greater, while the total commercial supply of fuel and power of all kinds is about one-fifteenth of the required input.

These commercial sources are not free and, with the exception of hydroelectricity, they are not replenished. Our coal and oil represent "bottled sunshine" of millions of years ago and, although new fields are being discovered all the time, they are capital that we squander only at the expense of future generations. They represent potential raw materials for the chemical industry. It may be that in a couple of hundred years or so we shall have denuded the easier sources of these fossil fuels. There is also a geographical disadvantage in reliance on them, for those countries not blessed with rich reserves.

Even the advent of nuclear energy from fission has not transformed the prospects, although some scientists, who have presumably not done the sums, have hailed it as *the* means of escaping from reliance on the land for food production. But providing the energy input for food production would require hundreds of tons of uranium a day. As the world's known reserves of readily accessible uranium, in the form of rich ores, are only of the order of a few million tons, we could only sustain such output for a very few years. There is more thorium, which can also be converted into nuclear fuel in a reactor, but that too would not last long at such consumption rates.

We are therefore compelled to look at the "last-resort" source of fission fuel: the uranium and thorium present in ordinary rock. As Professor Harrison Brown has observed (*The Challenge of Man's Future*, Secker & Warburg, 1954), the small traces of uranium and thorium in average granite are such that if they were all extracted from one ton of rock and "burned" in a nuclear reactor, the energy release would be equal to that obtained from burning about fifty tons of coal. He goes on to estimate that economical extraction might yield from a ton of rock a "net profit" of energy equivalent to seven tons of coal, at a processing cost of ten dollars. The uranium so produced would be two hundred times as expensive as uranium from ore, but still cheap compared with its coal equivalent.

Applying these estimates to our food requirements, however, it turns out that by this route we are replacing one cumbersome activity (agriculture) by another (uranium and thorium extraction). We should have to quarry and process millions of tons of rock *every day* to meet the demand for fuel replenishment; to set up the reactors and provide them with their initial fuel charge we should need to process several million million tons of rock. Our children's children may be obliged to take such ideas seriously, to meet their general power needs, but as an alternative to agriculture we have plainly strayed into farce. How much simpler to scatter a few seeds than to grind up the Himalayas!

Nuclear energy will make more sense in this connection if controlled fusion reactions become possible. Water is a more manageable substance than rock, and the heavy hydrogen which it contains can in principle yield virtually unlimited power. But we have no guarantee that practical methods of converting this heavy hydrogen to useful power will indeed be devised in the foreseeable future (although no one can seriously doubt that one day the problem will be solved) and in any case they may prove to be expensive. It would be foolish to base the idea of a switch from agriculture on so hypothetical a source of energy.

Hydro-electric power is not the answer, either, for food manufacture. If all the suitable rivers were applied to this purpose—to the detriment, may it be said, of much wild scenery—their combined output would be too little by far to meet the world's food requirements.

So we come back to sunlight. The total energy arriving from the Sun at the Earth's outer atmosphere is more than three million million million Calories per day, but scattering and absorption within the atmosphere greatly reduces the energy arriving at the surface. At any one place on the ground, depending on weather, time of day and season, the energy may vary from zero to 7,500 Calories per square metre per day. For a huge area of the world's land between latitudes 35° N and 35° S, one can reckon on an average of nearly 5,000 Calories per square metre per day. Farrington Daniels (*Direct Use of the Sun's Energy*, Yale, 1964) draws attention to the North Chilean salt desert, which has 364 days a year of bright sunshine over 28,000 square miles and receives 360 million million

Calories per day, substantially more than all the heat released in the world by burning coal, oil, gas, and wood.

The radiation in higher latitudes is less, but the disparity can be reduced by using tilted collection surfaces. Moreover, by the tests of agricultural production, using sunlight, it is clear that regions in the higher latitudes such as north-west Europe are far from being a write-off merely because bright sunshine occurs infrequently.

Let us take a cautious average figure of 2,500 Calories per square metre per day, for purposes of calculation. Then, if we could devise a sun-powered food-producing system with an overall efficiency of 5 per cent, the area of sunlight-collector required is forty square metres (or one-hundredth of an acre) per head, or 360,000 square kilometres (140,000 square miles) for a world population of 9,000 million.

It is hard to believe that non-chemical methods of capturing the energy of sunlight can be cheap enough in terms of capital cost for the quite large collecting surfaces required. Existing solar cells, for example, as used in Earth satellites for generating electricity from sunlight, give an efficiency of 12 per cent, and cost (1961 figure) about £7,000 per square metre. It is possible that advances in semiconductor technology will bring down costs markedly, and improve efficiencies, but it is unlikely to serve for the poorer nations. The large concave mirror with a boiler or other converter at the moving focus is also an unlikely candidate, especially as it is no use when the sky is overcast. Other dodges, such as thermoelectric converters, which generate electricity from a temperature difference created by sunlight, are also not very plausible. There is a fundamental reason for avoiding energy conversion systems that depend on heat. It arises from thermodynamics, and can be expressed in simple terms by saying that the "quality" of energy is as important as the quantity. Sunlight is energy of high quality (simply because the surface of the Sun is quite hot); so is electricity and chemical energy. Heat energy, on the other hand, is only as "good" as the temperature with which it is associated. There is plenty of useless heat energy in cold water. To employ sunlight to heat something—water, say, or a thermoelectric junction—through a few degrees is a shocking waste.

If, on the other hand, we can find chemical methods of capturing sunlight analogous to those used in green plants not only are they more likely to be cheap in themselves but also may perform the first stages of the synthesis of food.

On the assumption, then, that other solar energy converters are likely to be too expensive, the overriding aim should be the search for more efficient ways of using sunlight to create chemical energy. We should not underestimate the difficulties of this task; if we are to improve on nature in this respect we should recognize how ingenious nature is, in the green plant. But we should also bear in mind that success in this direction would not only be rewarding for food production; if efficient chemical sunlight-collectors are developed they should also find application for general power supplies.

The process of photosynthesis in a green plant is, in importance and ingenuity, one of the supreme triumphs of blind evolution. It enables the plant to grow using primarily water and carbon dioxide—very simple and accessible raw materials. The overall process is:

$$\text{carbon dioxide} + \text{water} \rightarrow \text{sugar} + \text{oxygen}$$

When we consider that if we make the reaction go the other way, by burning sugar in oxygen, we get a substantial release of energy, it should be plain that a pretty massive input of energy is necessary to bring about the synthesis of sugar. The remarkable thing about natural photosynthesis is that the packets of light energy from the Sun, the photons, are individually too feeble to bring about this reaction. Nature has devised the means of adding up the energy of several photons in order to convert one molecule of carbon dioxide into carbohydrate.

The details of the natural process of photosynthesis which takes place in intricate little bodies within the plant cells, called chloroplasts, are complicated and in some respects still obscure. What happens can be outlined in four main stages: (1) the absorption of sunlight by plant pigments, chiefly the chlorophylls; (2) the transfer of the energy to chemical reagents, called NADP and ATP; (3) the action of these reagents in breaking down water to hydrogen and oxygen and reacting the hydrogen with carbon dioxide, and (4) the "follow-through" in which sugars (and other materials) are elaborated. The energy economy is good, once the sunlight is absorbed, especially when we take account of the fact that the photons of red light, of relatively low energy, will do the trick as well as more energetic yellow or blue light. For red light, the efficiency is about 30 per cent. When we consider that a series of about a hundred chemical processes are probably involved, this figure for natural photosynthesis is astonishingly high. On the other hand, not much of the sunlight is absorbed in the first place.

We have set ourselves the target of an overall efficiency of 5 per cent for primary food production from sunlight, 365 days a year. Whatever the details of the stages after the initial photosynthetic process, we have to aim for as high an efficiency as possible at the first step. There is a choice between the use of the highly organized photo-synthetic apparatus of living plants (either in complete organisms or in extracts), the simplification of the natural photosynthetic process to one or two basic steps, and the development of largely artificial analogues to the natural process. It is too early to be sure which of these courses may prove in the end to be best, or whether some quite different approach will turn out to be necessary. Something can be said about the possible details and apparent merits of the various approaches.

We are looking for round-the-year efficiency much higher than that of any crops customarily used in agriculture. The most efficient of the "normal" crops is generally held to be sugar cane, which in Hawaii is produced at a rate of 9·4 grams of dry organic matter per square metre per day, which corresponds to about 30 Calories per square metre per day, or about 0·6 per cent efficiency in the use of solar energy. Cultivation of algae in tanks to which additional carbon dioxide has been added has yielded for short favourable periods more than 40 grams, or about 160 Calories per square metre per day—slightly above 3 per cent efficiency. While such a rate is encouraging to the general idea that still higher efficiencies may be possible, there is little chance that algae themselves will provide the answer we are looking for. Efficiency of this level is achieved only by using small cultures at low light levels. Chlorophyll contents of typical natural communities are of the order of one gram of chlorophyll per square metre and evolution of oxygen (an index of photosynthesis carried out) is of the order of one gram of oxygen per gram of chlorophyll per hour. One gram of evolved oxygen corresponds to about $2\frac{1}{2}$ Calories of sugar formed, compared with sunlight falling at 500 Calories or more in an hour.

At one gram of chlorophyll per square metre there are ample chlorophyll molecules for each photon to have a very good chance of encountering a chlorophyll molecule. The low efficiency and slow rate of production must therefore arise because the photosynthetic process is a little slow. Half the energy in light is of wave-lengths unsuitable for absorption, and more energy is lost through inefficiency at subsequent stages and in reflection or absorption of light by other material in the plants, but it still means that for every photon which activates a chlorophyll molecule many which might do so fail to, because the chlorophyll molecules are "occupied".

Further thought is needed if we are to see how to get substantially greater production rates. Unless we can exploit much more chlorophyll in a given area than nature does, or recover the energy and restore the molecules to their receptive state much faster, the prospects for increasing the production rates are not bright.

On the first score, we might use much more chlorophyll (or chloroplasts) per square metre and stir vigorously, thus exposing fresh chlorophyll repeatedly. On the second possibility—recovering the energy faster—it seems likely that a more disorganized man-made system is, on the contrary, more likely to be slower than nature. Someone may be able to see how to adapt the natural mechanism of photosynthesis to make substantially more efficient use of the available sunlight; it seems to me, however, that additional supplies of carbon dioxide would be necessary and the natural machinery might well become clogged with the products of the reaction.

There are, indeed, philosophical reasons for doubting the "improvability" of natural photosynthesis. About 1 per cent of the solar energy falling on the land is fixed in plants, which is remarkably high if we consider that plants do not have to be efficient. What is more important is their ability to grow fast. H. T. Odum and E. P. Odum (*Fundamentals of Ecology*, Saunders, 1959) have used the analogy that it might be more important to reach a destination quickly at fifty miles per hour than to achieve maximum efficiency in fuel consumption by driving slowly. These ecologists also observe that it is not fair to compare engines and biological systems unless one considers the energy used in repairing and replacing machines, because biological systems are self-repairing and self-perpetuating. They are pessimistic about increasing basic efficiency in living systems as a means of increasing world food supply.

Living organisms have evolved in an environment in which the supply of sunlight is only one of the limiting factors. If we imagine a plant which could make much more efficient use of sunlight it would find nowhere natural to live where it could exploit its faculty. Conceivably, by selective breeding in artificial environments we could force the development of more efficient photosynthesis, but the gains are not likely to be as dramatic as those for which we are hoping.

My own hunch is that we shall do better to look for some different photochemical system—that is to say, another arrangement for building up chemical energy from sunlight. To pursue the Odums' analogy, we still need to drive at fifty miles an hour, but use a more efficient engine.

There is discouragement, however, in the complexity of

the system nature has found necessary, and also in the view that something as simple and straightforward as we are searching for should already be pretty obvious. Obvious it is not, but on the credit side we can say that our knowledge of the interactions of light with materials has been advancing rapidly. The development of the laser may not be directly relevant to the present aim, but at least it dramatizes the surprising possibilities that emerge from better understanding of reactions of materials with light.

The requirements can be specified fairly closely. We need a system using cheap materials which can absorb a large fraction of the energy of sunlight (visible light covers the wave-lengths 0·39 to 0·75 micrometres) and convert it into chemical form. If the chemical products are directly relevant to human food, so much the better.

As mentioned in connection with natural photosynthesis, the energy of the photons of sunlight is too little to bring about direct conversion of water and carbon dioxide into sugar: several photons have to be combined to this end. The dissociation of water into hydrogen and oxygen—the crucial step—requires ultraviolet radiation of wave-length 0·23 micrometres or shorter for direct accomplishment: although the Sun emits such radiation it does not penetrate the Earth's atmosphere. Whatever serves for our sunlight-collector, it must be capable of responding to the somewhat limited energy of the photons. Many reactions of well-known materials are excluded from consideration for this reason.

Nature suggests some interesting possibilities to us. Throughout the plant and animal kingdoms one relatively simple material serves as "common coin" for the transfer of energy from one biochemical process to another. It is adenosine triphosphate (ATP). It can give up its energy, along with one of its three phosphate groups, very conveniently in many different situations. It thereby changes to adenosine diphosphate (ADP) which, when it is exposed to a suitable source of energy, can reacquire a phosphate group and so become "recharged" with energy. The "spare" energy of each ATP molecule corresponds to a photon of infra-red radiation of wavelength of about 2·5 micrometres—much feebler than those of visible light so that, *in principle*, every photon of sunlight could "charge" an ATP molecule. In pursuing this line of thought we are accepting a maximum *theoretical* efficiency of only about 20 per cent—unless we want to envisage a complicated system whereby each of the more energetic photons produces more than one ATP molecule.

ATP is not the only high-energy phosphate compound used as an energy carrier in living systems. For example, the substances 1, 3-diphosphoglycerate and acetyl phosphate have about 50 per cent more available energy and would, in principle, be somewhat more efficient captors of solar energy.

While we may take hints like this from nature, there is, of course, a huge range of chemical reactions that have no particular place in living systems. The choice of the end-product of the primary light-fixing reaction is not too important: exchanges of chemical energy from one form to another can certainly be contemplated using wholly artificial means; moreover, micro-organisms are known to science that can exploit diverse materials as energy sources. One general tendency is indicated to us, however. "Food", in its very broadest sense, like combustible fuels such as coal and oil, is chemically "reduced" material—that is to say, oxygen has been driven out of the food materials with the expenditure of energy, so that on recombination with oxygen, in fermentation or respiration, energy can be recovered. In natural photosynthesis, water is reduced to hydrogen and oxygen is released. At an early stage in artificial food production we have to remove oxygen, or something chemically analogous, such as sulphur or chlorine. If we do that, we are making reduced material.

The trick for improving on living plants may involve the use of carefully matched pigments and reactive materials, so that light energy absorbed by the pigments is transferred to chemical form before it can be lost in the form of heat or fluorescent light re-emitted by the pigment. We shall probably have to do it without the elaborate structures and reaction cycles available to living plants, but selected enzymes or inorganic catalysts will probably be needed to make the reactions go fast enough to be useful.

Farrington Daniels, already quoted on the Chilean desert, observes: "No really practical photochemical reaction is yet available for storing the energy of the Sun or converting it into work, but there is no theoretical reason to deny the possibility." There are sufficient examples of "interesting" reactions brought about by light to encourage the belief that something will indeed be found.

One has been studied by Eugene Rabinowitch. When water containing the purple dye thionine and a ferrous salt is illuminated, the thionine is reduced to colourless leukothionine. Over a period of minutes the colour returns. If electrodes are put in the water, an electric current can be drawn.

Another of Daniels' examples is a reaction explored by

O. S. Neuwirth and others. Nitrosyl chloride is a substance which absorbs sunlight efficiently and is thereby broken up into nitric oxide and atomic chlorine. Its chief drawback is that much of the energy so captured is lost when chlorine atoms spontaneously pair up to make chlorine molecules.

We only need one good, simple reaction, driven by daylight, to transform the prospects for the human race along the lines outlined in this book. It will be worth looking for.

$4.95
EWNG

EDEN WAS NO GARDEN

An Inquiry into the Environment of Man

BY NIGEL CALDER

A great deal has been written in the last few years about human survival in 2000 A.D. Though the turn of the century is a frighteningly close thirty years from now, the population on our ravaged planet will, by that time, have doubled.

Rarely has anyone written on this subject more wisely, wittily, or convincingly than has Nigel Calder in EDEN WAS NO GARDEN. He suggests a remarkably complete program for replenishing and restoring what is "still the kindliest place we know," to support the soon-to-be-born millions. The book explores the deadly game of human and terrestrial survival and, while it is not an alarmist tract, it does amplify the grim and complex details of the imminent disaster which confronts us—unless we begin to study closely the bewildering range of opportunities open for our salvation. As Mr. Calder reminds us, "Men are now able to do pretty much what they put their minds to . . ." Yet, we are apparently helpless to do anything much about protecting our environment.

We must rediscover our own planet as conscientiously and with the same sense of wonder as we are now preparing to explore Mars and the other planets of the solar system. Just as the engineers of the forthcoming Voyager spacecraft have to ensure, regardless of cost, absolute perfection, so our human operations on earth must henceforward be undertaken

(Continued on back flap)